Simon Dunning

July 2015

Stephen of Linthouse

Stephen of Linthouse

A SHIPBUILDING MEMOIR 1950–1983

Alexander M M Stephen

IESIS

INSTITUTION OF ENGINEERS
AND SHIPBUILDERS IN SCOTLAND

IESIS

First published in 2015 by
Institution of Engineers and Shipbuilders in Scotland
16 Robertson Street,
Glasgow, Scotland
G2 8DS

ISBN 978-0-9932048-0-7

British Library Cataloguing-in-Publication Data
A catalogue record for this book is available from
the British Library

Typeset by Mark Blackadder

Printed and bound Claro Print, Glasgow

Contents

Acknowledgements

Without the collection of Stephen and shipbuilding family papers meticulously filed and preserved by my late brother Jim, I would not have attempted to write this book and without the vital minutes and records which Ron Barclay preserved when the company was being wound down, the task would have been even harder. David Watson provided invaluable information on ships built after 1950 in order to allow the most complete list of Stephen built ships to be compiled. Iain and Barbara MacLeod have proofread and given me enormous help. Finally my greatest supporter and sternest critic, my wife Sue has made many suggestions which have greatly improved this book.

For the illustrations I have to thank Glasgow University Archives for providing plates 8, 9, 12–15, 17, 22, 25–32, 67. Fred Walker and Mrs Gwen Hudd provided the photographs for plates 18–21, the National Geographical Society plate 23, Glasgow Museums plate 59, Imperial War Museum plate 69 and the Scottish Maritime Museum plate 70. The remainder are reproduced by courtesy of the Stephen family, with my son Graham playing a major part. The quotations are stolen from William Shakespeare.

Dedicated to the loyal people at Linthouse
with whom I was proud to work.

Foreword

Speak what we feel not what we ought to say – King Lear

Industrial histories are usually about success and two books about the Stephen shipyards have already been written. Many fine achievements of Alexander Stephen & Sons have been recorded in *A Shipbuilding History 1750–1932*, put together largely by my father Murray Stephen, and written from the shipbuilder's point of view, whereas, in *Stephen of Linthouse 1750–1950* John Carvel has looked at the Company from the outside. What I have added contains little about success and deals with the decline and fall of the Company in which I was involved during the latter years.

While the Stephen enterprise was being wound up and shareholders repaid in 1983, I retrieved what Company papers and books I could and put them in my attic, and when my brother Jim died ten years later his papers were added. At that time I was fully occupied looking after 80 acres and only when I had downsized to quarter of an acre in 2006 was I able to study the archives. I had intended to use them to write a straight sequel to *Stephen of Linthouse*, but it would have made very depressing reading. Failures can be brushed aside in a success story but when little is going well they assume centre stage, so I have tried to add a more personal touch with the happier side of shipbuilding and relieve the pain with a dash of humour. While I have recorded the things which went wrong, my unrecorded memories 50 years later are of outstanding people and magnificent ships which were built with few troubles and served their owners for many years.

Though my memory of events may not be perfect, I will stand by the opinions I have expressed. However inadequate my writing may be, this book concerns a family enterprise dating from 1750 and contains an important contribution to shipbuilding history by recording every vessel built from 1813 as the score of Stephen launches could rightfully challenge the 'thousand ships' attributed to fair Helen of Troy.

When I hung the portraits of my shipbuilding ancestors in my home, I feared that, they would come out of their frames one night and condemn me for destroying the famous company they had created, but while I take my share of blame, I realise now that the downfall of the British Shipbuilding Industry was unavoidable.

A M M Stephen
Balfron 2015

CHAPTER 1

Linthouse in 1950

Admit me chorus to this history – Henry V

In 1950 Glasgow was a drab colourless city, its fine Victorian buildings blackened by decades of soot laden fog which paralysed the city every winter. Hundreds of factory chimneys and thousands of domestic fires belched out black smoke creating the most appalling fogs in winter. Glasgow's people were tired from the war with shortages and food rationing which was to continue for another four years. Rationing had, however, imposed a new discipline on eating habits, giving a better balanced diet and twelve years of full employment had given a higher standard of living than ever known before. The backstreets of Govan no longer swarmed with hungry, ragged and barefooted children and better food meant that the 'bowly' legs caused by rickets were becoming a thing of the past.

In thick fog all traffic except the trams and the subway came to a halt. As a child I remember being driven in the dark through the middle of Glasgow to a family Christmas party. Near the Clyde visibility was so bad that my mother had to get out and walk in front of the car. She followed the tramlines which she could see in the car's headlights while my father drove the car slowly, following her pale silk stockinged legs. The tramlines were a blessing – so were silk stockings. We got to the party somewhat late, avoiding the error many motorists made of finishing up in the tram depot.

The Whiteinch ferries delivered their occupants onto Holmfauld Road which ran through Alexander Stephen & Sons' land. The vehicular ferry was a large rectangular pontoon with a propeller at each corner. Above it a vehicle deck was jacked up and down as the tide rose and fell. The passenger ferries, which had changed little since they first started, were small double ended open boats which nosed up to wooden steps in a bell shaped recess. As everybody wanted to get off quickly, they moved towards the bow which made steering difficult so the ferry often hit the side before reaching the steps and caused unwary passengers to lose their balance. Old John Stephen, my great-great-uncle and Chairman of the Company from 1899–1916, used the ferry every day travelling between his home in Partick and Linthouse. On one occasion he jumped for the steps too soon, slipped and was totally immersed. He was fished out, taken to the Gatehouse and hosed down thoroughly before being dried out, apparently none the worse for his experience. In my time anybody who fell into the river was taken to hospital to be given a tetanus injection even though the water was less foul than when John sampled it. The ferries had problems in foggy weather. To check their position in midstream the noisy steam engines were stopped and the helmsman listened for a bell which was rung on the far side of the river. On one occasion the passenger ferry picked up the noise from the wrong bell and homed in on a dredger anchored half a mile down stream. The ferry eventually made port but instead of three minutes, the crossing took an hour and a half. When living near Anniesland, I travelled to work at Linthouse by bicycle and preferred to take the vehicular ferry to avoid having to carry a bicycle down the slippery steps to the passenger ferry.

Britain was nearly bankrupt. Huge debts incurred during the war were being paid back so everything possible was exported. The highest earners paid Income Tax at the rate of 95% and it was said that Sir James Lithgow once tipped a porter a coin saying "Here's a pound for you, less tax" and dropped a sixpence into his hand. For the first time ever, taxation hit the whole workforce and killed the 'squad system' in the shipyards. This had worked well particularly in the Black Squad, as the steelworkers were called. A squad of riveters or platers consisted of five or six people, very often from one family[1]. At the end of the week the squad leader was given the total earnings and he distributed the money as he saw fit. Squads sometimes included a mentally retarded family member who contributed little and would be paid accordingly, but he went home every Friday with earned money in his pocket and with pride. Nowadays the 'minimum wage' rules out this form of employment, and the taxpayer provides institutions where these people lead less fulfilling lives.

Almost everything was in short supply. Though clothes were no longer rationed most of what was available was 'utility' and inevitably dull. Household items were scarce. Although ships counted as 'export' and were given priority, everything was hard to come by. No shipyard dared start building a passenger ship unless enough teak for decking and handrails was already in stock. Alexander Stephen's had just lightened the gloom by celebrating their Bicentenary with dinners for customers and staff and the book *Stephen of Linthouse 1750–1950* was widely distributed.

We were a medium sized shipyard with a workforce between 3,500 and 4,000 ranking alongside Scotts of Greenock and Hawthorn Leslie on the Tyne, and much smaller than John Brown's which employed about 10,000. Our Board had been unchanged for the best part of a generation but was still progressive. My father was Chairman and Managing Director and had a firm grip of the company finances and the process of estimating, which he maintained to be the most important factor in shipbuilding. My uncle John Stephen, the Shipyard Director, was striving to achieve an efficient change-over from

1. For generations the Orr family ran the Frame Squad which heated steel frames in a furnace and bent them to suit the hull. I worked alongside Bert Orr in the Ship Drawing Office.

riveting to welding, a task which was to continue for years. Shirley Ralston, the Naval Architect, was shortly to retire after almost 50 years with the Company. The Ralston Stability Indicator had become standard in every merchant ship and allowed a Captain to calculate how his cargo should be stowed to achieve satisfactory stability. Ralston was effective and had a keen sense of humour, particularly when pulling the legs of Engineers. Willie Johnstone had seen the Repair Department grow during the war when they had to repair ships with horrific damage. Immediately after the war up to 3,000 men had been employed reconverting troop ships back to carrying passengers. With no drydock facilities of its own, the Repair Department was thereafter limited to voyage repairs with the occasional refit. It was a small but highly effective part of the organisation. George Grange oversaw Engine Design and Drawing Office work. He had been awarded the DSO and MC in World War I and been a Director since 1926. He was a quiet retiring man who fitted in well and ran his outfit efficiently. However he surprised us all shortly before he retired when he became the owner of a zoomy yellow and red sports car. Alec MacLellan ran the Engine Works and had been a Director since 1916. He was also Chairman of Glenfield and Kennedy, the valvemakers in Kilmarnock, had captained Prestwick Golf Club and would later receive an Honorary Doctorate from Glasgow University. He was Murray and John's first cousin[2] and a gregarious person with an endless fund of stories.

Most of the workforce lived within walking distance of the Yard and flooded through the Shipyard and Engine Works entrances every day. Some came by ferry, a few cycled with a lesser number on motorcycles, but apart from Directors only two people owned motor cars. Glasgow Corporation trams, ending their journey in front of the Main Office, were packed with humanity at starting and stopping times. They were

2. See Family Tree opposite page 9.

mostly 'green' trams with a broad green band to denote the route they would take. Saturday morning working had stopped in 1947 but Christmas Day was still a full working day. I was a junior draughtsman in the Ship Drawing Office the following Christmas. John Stevenson, the Chief Draughtsman, called us together about 3 o'clock and told us we could leave quietly in small groups, making no noise, particularly when we passed the boardroom area. We crept out on tiptoe and I drove home to find my father already there. He roared with laughter when I told him the details of our early release and said all the Directors had left long before us.

Everybody from the Chairman down took their summer holidays at the Glasgow Fair when the Yard closed, leaving only the maintenance squads to overhaul the weary machinery. The popular holiday spots were on the Clyde coast with Rothesay being number one resort, so 'thoosands' of Glaswegians set off 'doon the watter' for two weeks. Few holidayed out of Scotland. Continental holidays were rare, with foreign currency being limited to £35 a year and air travel expensive and infrequent. Every manufacturing facility and almost every shop closed and Glasgow was deserted with only a skeleton transport service available. Smoke and fog then blew away when once a year the whole city could be seen clearly from the surrounding hills.

A twelve year run of warships had dried up and the Shipyard was building mainly refrigerated cargo liners for our old customers. We had lost one customer in Maclay & McIntyre who were tramp owners for whom we had built ships regularly before the war. Our finishing standards were higher than their requirements but building for them had been a useful exercise helping us achieve sensible savings. At the end of the war they had waited for a recession, hoping to order ships at low prices, but unlike 25 years earlier, it never came and they missed the boat. The founders were Lord Maclay, known as Holy Joe, who ran his fleet tightly and efficiently, and ThomasMcIntyre, the man of business and a skilful negotiator.

My father told me that when the Boer War started, shipping rates rocketed and Maclay broke a contract with a Glasgow shipbroker to take advantage of them. McIntyre was deputed to face the wrath of the shipbroker and had his argument well prepared, but was met with "Meester McIntyre, yer breeks is doon and we're going tae skelp ye".

In 1945 the Labour Party had swept into power with a large majority to carry out their manifesto which would transform society. The National Health Service, new laws to give adequate notice of dismissal and a national pension scheme were huge steps towards a fairer society, but some of these reforms would have happened earlier had it not been for the war. The Cabinet was almost half Trade Unionists most of whom were extremely able. The nationalisation of Industry was part of their programme with Coal and the Railways already taken into national custody and more industries threatened. In *Stephen of Linthouse* my father wrote "If, by any fell chance, the deadening, soul destroying and inefficient hand of nationalisation is ever laid on the shipbuilding industry, I, for one, would feel that all the efforts of my family, which have gone to make this Firm, had in the end proved vain". Nationalisation of the Industry would have been disastrous at that time. By the end of the war the Trade Unions were in a dominant position and five years of Labour government had further strengthened their hand so they were firmly in the driving seat.

In the Shipyard hand riveting had all but disappeared. A skilled hand squad could be poetry in motion. Two riveters, one hitting left handed, used light hammers with slender shafts about 2'6" long. They hit the end of the red hot rivet alternately with incredible precision and a newly flattened rivet end could be a thing of beauty. A pneumatic hammer, operated by one man, had replaced the two hand riveters (one of the few concessions the Boilermakers' Union ever accepted) but the glamour had gone. Even the heavy hammer of the 'hauder on' (holder on) which held the rivet head against the steel plate had been replaced by an air pressured cup. Riveters had been the kings amongst tradesman and the highest paid. Nobody disputed their authority as their upper body strength made it inadvisable. It was said that the older riveters turned up on a Monday morning with flowing white beards but by the end of the week their beards were black.

In the Directors' lunch room it was customary for a glass of sherry to be offered at a quarter to one. There were often visitors and when there were to be 13 at the table, any guests thought to be superstitious would be offered a second drink to dull their perception though it is surprisingly difficult to count 13 at a round table, even when completely sober. The table could seat fifteen and had a revolving dumb waiter in the middle so that anyone who was short of time could help themselves. Alcohol was forbidden elsewhere but on the afternoon of New Year's Eve a blind eye was turned. After working hours were shortened, the Yard closed at midday before Hogmanay in the expectation that everybody would work normally that morning, but the bottles merely appeared earlier.

One sad result of alcohol was the pathetic group of about twenty wives who stood outside the gates every Friday at stopping time. They were there to intercept their husbands before they drank their week's wages away in the local pub. 'Our' pub at the top of the road was the 'Gazelle' locally known as the 'Guzzle'. Next door Mr MacGregor the barber cut almost everybody's hair at 6d (2½p) a time and his shop was the local information centre. Mrs Gillies, the Linthouse postmistress for many years, took great pride in the company connection. Every August she telephoned Jim's secretary to remind him and me that it was time for us to get a new Game Licence, then a legal requirement for shooting. It must have been a status symbol to issue these licenses which were probably the only two sold in Govan.

In 1950 I was studying Engineering at Cambridge University having served almost three years in the Royal Navy.

THE STEPHEN SHIPBUILDERS – FAMILY TREE

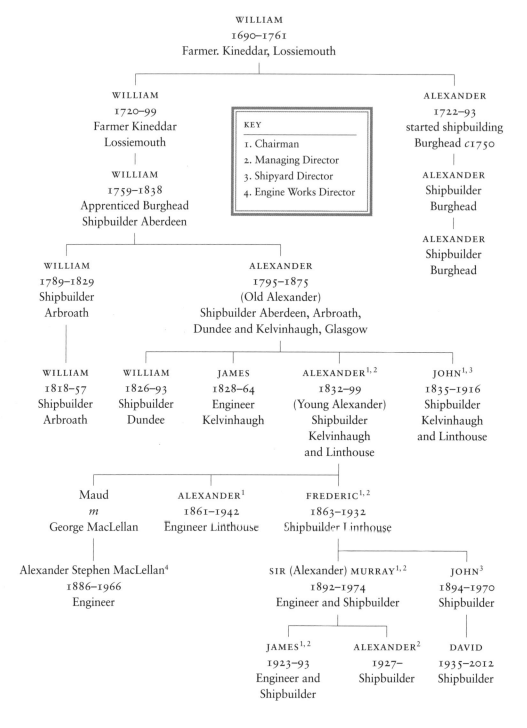

KEY

1. Chairman
2. Managing Director
3. Shipyard Director
4. Engine Works Director

- WILLIAM, 1690–1761, Farmer. Kineddar, Lossiemouth
  - WILLIAM, 1720–99, Farmer Kineddar Lossiemouth
    - WILLIAM, 1759–1838, Apprenticed Burghead Shipbuilder Aberdeen
      - WILLIAM, 1789–1829, Shipbuilder Arbroath
        - WILLIAM, 1818–57, Shipbuilder Arbroath
      - ALEXANDER, 1795–1875, (Old Alexander) Shipbuilder Aberdeen, Arbroath, Dundee and Kelvinhaugh, Glasgow
        - WILLIAM, 1826–93, Shipbuilder Dundee
        - JAMES, 1828–64, Engineer Kelvinhaugh
        - ALEXANDER[1,2], 1832–99, (Young Alexander) Shipbuilder Kelvinhaugh and Linthouse
          - Maud *m* George MacLellan
            - Alexander Stephen MacLellan[4], 1886–1966, Engineer
          - ALEXANDER[1], 1861–1942, Engineer Linthouse
          - FREDERIC[1,2], 1863–1932, Shipbuilder Linthouse
            - SIR (Alexander) MURRAY[1,2], 1892–1974, Engineer and Shipbuilder
              - JAMES[1,2], 1923–93, Engineer and Shipbuilder
              - ALEXANDER[2], 1927–, Shipbuilder
            - JOHN[3], 1894–1970, Shipbuilder
              - DAVID, 1935–2012, Shipbuilder
        - JOHN[1,3], 1835–1916, Shipbuilder Kelvinhaugh and Linthouse
  - ALEXANDER, 1722–93, started shipbuilding Burghead *c*1750
    - ALEXANDER, Shipbuilder Burghead
      - ALEXANDER, Shipbuilder Burghead

CHAPTER 2

Early History

What's gone and what's past help – The Winter's Tale

The first two hundred years of Alexander Stephen & Sons' history is related elsewhere but summarised here. The earlier books had to avoid offending customers so some pertinent happenings were omitted but, with the Company wound up years ago, history can now be related 'warts and all' and skeletons brought out of cupboards. If only he were here today, my father's fund of shipbuilding stories would have added spice to this Stephen saga.

Alexander Stephen (1722–93)[1] was the second son of a tenant farmer at Kineddar near Lossiemouth in Moray. As his elder brother inherited the tenancy, he became a shipbuilder and started his own shipyard at nearby Burghead about 1750. Little is known about this yard except that his son and grandson, both Alexanders, carried on the business. Alexander's nephew William (1759–1838) joined him but left to learn Naval Architecture in Aberdeen[2]. He set up his own shipyard there at Footdee[3] in 1793. He built brigs, schooners and snows[4]

1. There was a surfeit of Alexanders and Williams but the Family Tree opposite should help the reader distinguish them. I am proud to be an Alexander Stephen although, following Scottish tradition, as a second son, I was named after my maternal grandfather. The names by which my ancestors were known within the family are not generally known, but I share 'Sandy' with my great-great-grandfather Alexander.
2. His apprenticeship agreement is in the Stephen archives.
3. Pronounced 'Fittie' locally.
4. A 'snow' was a type of the two masted sailing ship built at that time.

up to 236 tons and employed up to 30 men. In the earlier Stephen books the first ship was recorded as *Erol Fife* but, when I later visited Aberdeen, the Maritime Museum produced a longer list of ships which rejected the local dialect and recorded the ship correctly as *Earl of Fife*. Old plans, also produced by the Aberdeen Maritime Museum, show that William first rented about a quarter of an acre of foreshore next to Pocra Point in Aberdeen harbour and later took on two other similar areas and a timber yard. An 1824 plan shows a 'duelling house' [sic] in the corner of the first plot which must be where he originally lived.

William ran his business successfully but acted as guarantor for his eldest son, also William, who had set up his own shipyard in Arbroath. Young William put some bad timber into one of his ships, was sued and lost the lawsuit. He was declared bankrupt and brought his 69 year old father down with him. The extremely able second son Alexander took over and soon paid off his father's debts. Running two shipyards 60 miles apart was difficult so he sold the Aberdeen yard and developed Arbroath, building schooners and brigs up to 200 tons and employing 130 men. In 1837 Alexander moved to Dundee and further expanded the business, building ships up to 1,000 tons and employing 400 men. His nephew William took over the Arbroath yard but died at the age of 39. The enterprising Alexander realised that the future lay in iron ships and that Dundee was a long way from the nearest ironworks. In 1850 he left his eldest son William to run the Dundee yard and took a 20 year lease of Kelvinhaugh Shipyard in Glasgow near where the Kelvin flows into the Clyde and just west of the present Scottish Exhibition Centre.

Alexander moved to Glasgow with his wife and large family where he bought two adjoining houses in St. Vincent Crescent near the shipyard and knocked them into one. He had eighteen children all by the same wife. Two daughters had died young in accidents but, remarkably for those days, the other sixteen reached adulthood. James Templeton, who married one of the daughters, described the Stephens as 'a happy family with much laughter'.

The Company forged ahead building ships up to 2000 tons occasionally launching 10 ships in a year. Alexander, with retirement in mind, kept his options open on which of his sons should succeed him – James, the Engineer or Alexander, the Naval Architect who was four years younger. The matter resolved itself when ship number 9, *Euphrates*, failed to make the specified speed in 1855. The engineering was clearly at fault and James was responsible. He failed to get the matter put right, took to the bottle and was eventually sacked. Having already fathered an illegitimate child he was a liability so, as the black sheep of the family, he was packed off to America on an allowance. To the family's horror he came back again and married his first cousin, an alliance thoroughly disapproved of. After she died he married his housekeeper by whom he had two sons. James died at Moffat aged 36. His youngest brother John then acted *in loco parentis* to the two boys and paid for their upbringing. John's own two children had died young and his unfortunate wife then gave birth to nine stillborn babies almost certainly due to the rhesus factor.

Before the lease of Kelvinhaugh ran out in 1870 Old Alexander bought the Linthouse estate on the south bank of the Clyde where the tunnel now runs under the river. Turning a country estate into a shipyard did not meet with universal approval as 'The Old Country Houses of the Old Glasgow Gentry' eulogises about the illustrious owners of Linthouse, but ends "Linthouse was afterwards sold to Mr Steven [sic], who has cut down the fine old trees and made the place into a shipbuilding yard, the Mansion House itself being turned into offices connected therewith". A watercolour of the Clyde at Linthouse[5] before the river was dredged makes me sympathise

5. Plate 48.

with the conservationists, but if the Stephens hadn't developed the site, others would have done.

Having masterminded the layout of the new shipyard Old Alexander retired to his beloved Dundee and helped his son William at the shipyard there. The Dundee yard had built up a great reputation for steam driven whalers and sealers. Best known is *Terra Nova*[6] which was built in 1884 and converted to take Captain Scott's ill fated expedition to the Antarctic 26 years later. Shackleton used *Aurora* and *Nimrod* in his Antarctic forays. William also built clippers including *Maulesden*[7] which sailed from Greenock to Maryborough in Queensland in 70 days, a record never reached by any other sailing ship. He was also successful as a shipowner but when he died in 1893 the Dundee shipyard was sold as a management buyout.

Young Alexander took over at Linthouse assisted by his brother John. The second half of the nineteenth century was a period of great prosperity for Glasgow and the brothers built up the business to become one of the major shipyards on the Clyde with its own Engine Works. In some years the tonnage launched at Linthouse exceeded that of any other Clyde yard.

James was not the only black sheep of the family, the other being the fourth brother Andrew who became a Doctor and practised in London. Andrew lived in great comfort but spent most of his inheritance and then demanded more money from his father. There were bitter quarrels and on one occasion his father physically threw him out of his house. Andrew became so embittered he determined to do his family down. He had posters printed defaming the Stephens and hired a billposter to stick them up in Linthouse and Govan, so the family had to hire another man to tear them down. Andrew and his son Ernest took the train from London to Glasgow once a year to walk the right-of-way which passed along the riverside at Lint-

6. Plate 23.

7. Plate 55 shows her sister ship *Duntrune*.

house. The route consisted of a wooden walkway which ran round the sterns of the ships on the berths so that it had to be dismantled for every launch. Alexander and John were petitioning to have the right-of-way annulled while Andrew was determined to thwart his brothers, but their petition was eventually accepted. There were acrimonious lawsuits between Andrew and his father and other family members. The quarrel became really nasty when the young man accused his father of incest with his daughters but Andrew's siblings rallied round their father. Old Alexander's son-in-law the Reverend James Stewart[8], who was married to Mina the youngest of the family of eighteen, led the peacemaking and eventually the feud was settled. Ernest, the trouble maker's son, later worked briefly at Linthouse and my father said he was 'not a bad bloke'. The rebellious Andrew would seem to have finally reformed because his descendents include three Peers of the Realm.

In 1877 Young Alexander raised finance for four ships for the Clan Line, which Charles Cayser had built up. The Coats, Muir and Arthur families put up most of the capital with the promise of a handsome return but the venture was not as profitable as hoped, and they got nothing because the agreement stated that Cayser should first get a generous fixed percentage. There was acrimony between Cayser and his shareholders who received much sympathy in the West of Scotland. The story goes that this caused his sons to be shunned by Glasgow society and the Clan Line eventually moved to London though the family still have footholds in Scotland. My father, when a young man, met Cayser who was London born and had become a Baronet but still did have an 'aitch' to his name, though one of his sons, a friend of my father-in-law, was created Lord Rotherwick.

When Young Alexander died in 1899 his brother John

8. He was a famous missionary in Africa and later Moderator of the Free Church of Scotland.

took over the Chairmanship and Alexander's two sons, Alec the Engineer and Fred the Naval Architect, became the executive directors. They changed the focus of the Company towards passenger ships. After John died in 1916 Alec became less active and moved to Ayrshire while Fred, who was a modest man refusing a knighthood, ran the show. When he died in 1932 his son Murray became Chairman and Managing Director with his second son John, Shipyard Director. They survived the appalling slump of the early thirties, being saved by one contract. In 1930 an order for two 14,000 ton passenger ships *Corfu* and *Carthage* for the Peninsula & Orient Steam Navigation Company (P & O) was obtained against fierce competition and was expected to contribute little to the Company overheads. In the event the slump got deeper and these two ships were among the few building on the river. The cream of the Clyde labour force was available and taken on for the fitting out. They worked superbly even though each man knew that he would be on the dole as soon as his work was finished. The Company covered its overheads and even made a small profit.

The Company's first order from P & O had been in 1875 for the 3536 ton steamship *Nepaul*, closely followed by three 1075 ton sailing ships for New Zealand Shipping Company. One of these was *Piako*, the first of three of that name which we were to build for them at 45 year intervals, two of them pictured in plates 16 and 17. P & O and its subsidiaries were always the Company's main customers with New Zealand Shipping Company, British India Steam Navigation and Union Steamship Company of New Zealand all featuring regularly.

Lord Inchcape's buying control of Stephen's in 1918 was not mentioned in the Bicentenary book. He bought a majority of the ordinary and preference shares largely from Alec who, with four daughters, had less long term interest in the Company. Vertical integration was then quite common with Blue Funnel Line owning Caledon Shipyard and Clan Line

Greenock Dockyard, so it seemed a sensible course for the future of Linthouse. Inchcape had promised to give the company 'a good deal of his work' but it became harder to get P & O orders after that and Stephen's lost other good customers who would not place orders with a Company controlled by one of their competitors. My father told me of the protracted and tortuous negotiations in which he was involved to get the order of *Viceroy of India*[9] and how the contract was eventually signed at Inchcape's home at Glenapp Castle in Ayrshire. When Inchcape died during the slump in 1932 his shares were valued at a shilling each although he had paid £1 for them 14 years earlier. Murray and John were keen to buy them back although short of capital because their father had left all his money life-rented to their stepmother. P & O prevaricated but eventually the ordinary shares came back into the family in 1936 at £1 a share.

Murray and John took on large overdrafts and during the war they struggled in a period when taxation was penally high. In 1946 Alexander Stephen & Sons Limited became a public company with 60% of the ordinary shares being sold at £3 each. From a family point of view this was a good move as we became less dependent on the volatile shipbuilding industry and Murray and John were able to clear their debts. The Prudential Insurance Company became the biggest outside shareholder with 5% followed by Legal & General with 3%. Surprisingly the Church of England became the third largest and my father said in private "If the C of E is against gambling, why do they hold shares in a shipyard?" The newly acquired shareholders were surprisingly co-operative and backed the board provided the dividends were reasonable.

In the 1930s people travelled less but my father was continually on the go, mainly to London. On one occasion a meeting in Liverpool finished too late for him to catch the train back

9. Plates 58 and 59.

to Glasgow. Somebody mentioned that an air service to Glasgow had just started, so he telephoned the new Speke Airport. The girl who answered him said that he would just have time to catch the flight to Glasgow, so he took a taxi to the airport which was just a hut, a hanger and a field. The girl who had spoken to him on the telephone sold him his ticket and ushered him into a waiting room. She came back a few minutes later, took him out to the small plane on which he was the only passenger and showed him how to fasten his safety belt. She then got into the front and flew him up to Glasgow. Apart from the mechanic who removed the chocks he saw nobody else.

Murray oversaw the company through the slow recovery of the 1930s and then endured the stressful years of the War when he spent about 60 nights a year in sleeper trains between Glasgow and London but he was well looked after because he was a Director of LMS railways. Unexpected pressures were put on the Company. Lord Beaverbrook was Minister of Aircraft Production from 1940 to 1942 and was determined to get what he wanted. He persuaded our already stretched Engine Works into accepting a large order for aero engine parts and promised plans and patterns. Although we chased the Ministry for these, we received nothing before the due delivery date. Beaverbrook then sent my father a personal telegram castigating him for failure to deliver and ending "The safety of the country is in your repeat your hands. Beaverbrook". A long telegram was sent back detailing what the Ministry had failed to do ending "Regret the safety of the country still in your repeat your hands. Stephen". The next day one of Beaverbrook's minions came to the Yard and asked for his boss's telegram back. History does not relate if he got it. Beaverbrook also requisitioned Alec MacLellan, the Engine Works Director, for an important job in his Ministry in London.

From 1936 to the end of the war in 1945 Stephen's were

principally engaged in building warships – an aircraft carrier, 3 cruisers, 2 fast minelayers and numerous destroyers, sloops and other smaller vessels. The sloop *HMS Amethyst*[10] achieved the greatest fame by sailing up the Yangtse River in 1949 in an attempt to protect British nationals who were trapped in Shanghai by the Chinese civil war. Chinese Communist gun batteries on the north bank opened fire on her and she was severely damaged with her captain and others killed, but she anchored safely. The destroyer. *HMS Consort*,[11] also Linthouse built, tried to rescue her but had to retreat due to severe damage and casualties. *Amethyst* seemed to be doomed, but after many days she was made fit to sail. One night after dark with her superstructure disguised she weighed anchor to slip in immediately astern of a brightly lit passenger ship which was going downstream. The Communist batteries failed to realise what was happening until too late and she then overtook the passenger ship and started on a perilous journey down the twisting and ill buoyed river. She passed all the danger points without a shot being fired at her and finally rejoined the fleet off the mouth of the river. Her dramatic escape was featured in the film 'Yangtse Incident' starring Richard Todd, a classic which is still repeated on television from time to time.

After the war, warships were no longer required and the focus changed to re-converting troopships back to passenger ships. This was highly labour intensive with the labour force rising to 5,000 at one time, but we soon reverted to building merchant ships, refrigerated cargo liners and the occasional passenger ship. P & O with its subsidiaries continued as our biggest customer but Elders & Fyffes, Ellerman and Elder Dempster were also rebuilding their fleets. The only orders from abroad had been for two refrigerated ships for Compag-

10. Plate 64.
11. *HMS Consort* was commanded by Commander Ian Robertson DSO, DSC and bar, whose son Nander is a friend and neighbour of mine.

nie General Transatlantique of France and one for the Argentine Government. Our output was limited by shortages of steel and almost all other materials, and our customers, desperate to make good their wartime losses, soon found a three year waiting list.

Since Noah's Ark shipbuilding has been an exciting profession and while at school it seemed to me a far more interesting prospect than just working in an office. I was intensely proud of the Shipyard and the fact that my father was a shipbuilder. Occasionally I visited Linthouse to be taken over a ship in its finishing stages. Although thrilled to be there, the noise and bustle was somewhat daunting. I was once taken to the French Polishers' Shop to collect one of my joinery efforts which they had very kindly polished for me and the smell of acetone which pervaded the shop remains in my memory even now.

The first launch I witnessed was *Rathlin* in 1936. It was a family affair as Alan Cuthbert, a Director of the Clyde Shipping Company for whom the ship was being built, had recently married my mother's sister Elspeth Mitchell who launched the ship and there was a lot of family ribbing at the lunch party after the launch. The next year I saw the launch of *Thendara*, a wooden auxiliary ketch of 87 tons, built for Sir Arthur Young, a double second cousin of my father, Chairman of Templeton's Carpets and Member of Parliament for Partick. The Linthouse launchways were more suitable for bigger vessels and the yacht stuck halfway down the slipway. This had been foreseen and a winch pulled her up the ways a little. She came free with a pop and was released to slide gracefully into the water.

The Stephen coat-of-arms was used to enhance the covers of the 1932 and 1950 books and was later emblazoned on all the Linthouse works gates as well as being used on letter heads. It had originally been registered with the Lord Lyon King of Arms as personal to Young Alexander Stephen about 1870. When the shipbuilding partnership was replaced by a limited company, its use was continued. This was actually illegal but nobody complained. Official registry of the coat-of-arms lapsed when Alexander's son Alec died, but it has since been resurrected in my name so its reproduction in this book should not be challenged.

My first experience in the shipyard was after leaving school in 1945 when I spent three months at Linthouse as a draughtsman (unpaid) in the Ship Design Office under David Watson who later became our much valued Naval Architect. It was a small and friendly office and the biggest job I had was calculating cargo capacities for the *Fort Richepanse* whose insulated holds were to carry bananas from the Caribbean to France. Later I worked in the Mould Loft, helping to draw ships' horizontal and vertical lines full size on a very large floor and fairing them until all the irregularities had been ironed out. It was an interesting but backbreaking job.

In the summer of 1950 the Anchor Line kindly took me on as a Supernumerary Engineer on *TSS Circassia*, a passenger/cargo ship with 200 passengers. Her Doxford diesel engines were showing their age and had to be dismantled regularly for minor repairs. This was ideal from my point of view as I learned a great deal about engines and how ships were run. The only serious crisis was when we were crossing the Indian Ocean and the port engine started to overheat due to cracked piston rings. It was stopped and taken apart to be repaired. To our horror the same thing then started to happen in the starboard engine. All three watches turned to and it was the only time I saw the Chief Engineer in his overalls. Midway through the frenzied activity he summoned me, instructed me to put on my whites, go up on deck and tell the passengers what good speed we were making. So much for my engineering ability! The port engine was repaired and in operation just before the overheated starboard engine became dangerous.

Circassia started in Glasgow and sailed to Liverpool, then through the Mediterranean and the Suez Canal. A stop at

Aden and Karachi came before three weeks at Bombay loading and unloading cargo and of course repairing the engines. I was lucky to have contacts there and even took part in some extremely lively Scottish Country Dancing in the middle of the monsoon while appropriately dressed in gym shoes and shorts. I got back to Britain just in time to start the autumn term at Cambridge having had the most unusual work experience of any of my fellow engineering students.

CHAPTER 3

Problems of Modernisation, 1950–54

Turning the accomplishments of many years into an hour glass – Henry V

Riveted ships were rapidly giving way to welded ships so spacious bays with high headroom were required for fabricating the large steel units. The foresight of Old Alexander and his son, who had designed the works in 1870, became apparent as the 80 year old building layout, shown in plate 33, fitted remarkably well. Steel rationing restricted us to launching about four ships a year and structural steel for the new buildings, which could have built several ships, had to come out of this ration. Two fabrication bays were built west of the Platers' Shed so that 60 ton units could be assembled under cover. To obtain a better production line the platers took over the adjoining Engine Boiler Shop and its crane gantry was extended to the west to make a modern stockyard, lifting plates by electromagnet. On the berths, the forest of derricks was replaced by three piers on each of which ran two 15 ton cranes on rails. As fabricated unit sizes increased, a 50 ton crane was added to each pier. Fewer building berths were required so No 1. Berth became redundant leaving five berths. The cranage on No. 6 berth was best with only one ship to service.

My Uncle John Stephen masterminded the shipyard modernisation. As American built all-welded Liberty Ships had sometimes broken in two, shipowners were at first reluctant to accept an all welded hull, so the transition to welding was a gradual process. Linthouse led the country in fabrication and we were feeling our way with all the other yards looking on. We were proud to take the lead but the next chapter will show how Trade Union intransigence made us regret having modernised.

Women had been taken on during the war as welders and many became very skilful, often better than the men, but at the end of the war the Boilermakers' Union decided it was a job for men only. The new methods required extra welders and experienced men were always in short supply, a problem which increased over the next twenty years. By limiting the numbers to be trained the Union maintained the shortage which kept welders' wage rates well above other trades. Blacksmiths' work, on the other hand, was decreasing as fittings previously forged had been redesigned for welding and mass production by specialist subcontractors.

Fitting out trades could not be modernised in the same way but new machinery was installed and shop layouts improved. New machines were relatively small, except for the plumbers' large pipe bending machine which could bend pipes up to 5" diameter. The trades we employed were joiners, electricians, plumbers, painters, sheet iron workers and deck engineers with the outside engineers fitting out the Engine Room. Tiling, terrazzo and pipe lagging work were subcontracted. Machinery and materials were put on board ships before the launch whenever possible because there was better cranage on the berths. Although fitting out trades did what they could before the launch, most man-hours were required at Shieldhall Wharf which was rented from the Clyde Trust[1]. We had built a fixed heavy crane for installing engines and a 15 ton travelling crane but these were sometimes inadequate. Our fitting out would have been better situated if the riverside mooring space nearest the shipyard had not been occupied by *Shieldhall* the Glasgow Corporation sewage boat[2]. The places of work were too

1. Later renamed Clyde Port Authority and later still Clydeport.
2. The Shieldhall Sewage Works adjoined the wharf and the sludge from the purification process was pumped each day into the sewage boat to be deposited off the Garroch Head south of the Isle of Bute.

spread out but that could not be avoided.

To replace what the shipyard plating department had taken over, a new boilershop had been built with gantry cranes lifting over 100 tons and increased headroom for large fabrications. The Engine Works Machine Shop was extended to the east in 1950 and to the west a few years later. Diesel engines, now more efficient and more powerful, were taking over from turbines so a new assembly bay and test bed were built. The modernisation of the Engine Works was completed in 1955 with a new pattern shop and store east of Holmfauld Road. Wooden patterns were a high fire risk and having them separate from the main buildings reduced insurance premiums.

The Machine Shop extension to the east had required the demolition of some of the 'Linthouse Buildings'. These well built tenement flats dated from 1870 when the shipyard had moved to a green field site, but some of the flats now restricted our development. As the national policy then was to demolish tenements, they were removed without any opposition. Twenty five flats nearest Govan Road, two shops and a small branch of the British Linen Bank remained untouched. Thereafter the buildings were managed by an estate agent and produced a small return, but the ability to house key workers was far more valuable to the Company.

Modernisation revealed an archaeological discovery. History related that before the Clyde was dredged, stepping stones had crossed the river at Linthouse. The name Linthouse means the 'house of the light, lint or lunt' and the original house by the river's edge had been obliged to show a light so that Govan revellers returning from the pubs in Partick could cross the river in safety at low tide. It was hard to believe that stepping stones had existed where a 60,000 ton vessel could now sail but when the new crane piers were being excavated, some of the old stepping stones were uncovered quite a distance from the river which had formerly been wider and shallower.

In 1952 K B Robinson, who had come to us from ICI with a good track record, was appointed a Director prior to taking over the Shipyard when Uncle John retired. 'KB', as he was known, planned the shipyard modernisation and put it into operation very successfully. A five storey Shipyard Office was built in 1954 to house shipyard staff, a planning department and a coding office, while the ground floor was to be occupied by our first computer. The Company Secretary John Haydock, who always wore a black jacket, striped trousers and a wing collar, had retired the same year. His place was taken by Norman Easton who had started the war as a conscientious objector and finished up in the Commandos with an MC. Norman was bright, energetic and a good leader and he set about modernising our accounting system with zest. Punched cards were used for our computer which was the size of a medium speed ship's diesel engine, with rows of thermionic valves, but with only a fraction of the power which is carried in one's pocket today. The savings were not enormous but good clerks were a dying breed and the future clearly lay with automation. Alec MacLellan and George Grange retired in 1954 and were replaced by Captain John D'Arcy RN combining the technical and production departments. John Robson took over from Shirley Ralston as Shipyard Technical Director and my brother Jim was appointed a Director to act as number two to D'Arcy.

Production continued to be limited by severe material shortages. Even in 1954, nine years after the end of the war, I visited Colvilles to beg for more steel only to be turned down flat. Delivery times were ridiculously long. The story goes that one of our ships was held up because we could not get a special high tensile steel bar to make six nuts which were essential for its Sulzer diesel engine. An apprentice, who had served in Fairfield's engine shop stores before joining us, approached Sam Paul, the Engine Works Manager, to say that there were plenty of these nuts in the Fairfield's store. With some cash in his pocket, the keen young man was helped over the wall between the two shipyards and returned with his pockets weighed down by the much valued nuts.

Always on the lookout for new products, we set up Fishing and Research jointly with Sir Denis Burney who had been knighted for his work on airships. This organisation planned to develop a mid water stern trawler. Traditional fishing nets scraped along the seabed but there was evidence that many shoals of fish swam at a higher level. Controllable 'otters', fitted on each side of a trawling net, were developed to keep it at the right depth. To begin with the otters were highly unstable, oscillating violently between surface and seabed. Eventually the technique was perfected but few fish were caught and the scheme was abandoned. A few years later radar was developed which could locate the shoals and the trawl could be adjusted before a run was made. We had missed out.

Bill Lochridge, a friendly man who had worked for Sir Denis and was a real 'Jack of all trades', joined us to fit into our organisation and occupy a wide variety of managerial posts.

When the Shipyard moved to Linthouse in 1870 the railway stopped at Govan so everything had to be taken by horse and cart for the last mile. Three years later the railway was extended to Shieldhall, a quarter of a mile west of the Yard. To get wagons from there to our internal railway system the Glasgow Corporation tram lines on Govan Road were used and our venerable steam locomotive hauled wagons to and from the Shieldhall siding. Nowhere else did a steam loco share a track with trams, so train buffs came from all over the world to take photographs. They even asked us to have the loco working on a Saturday afternoon. Some hope! Even in the early 1950s virtually all materials and machinery came by rail. An electric battery driven 'puggy' was bought to deal with the wagons, but the loco was still needed to take main engines, boilers and funnels to Shieldhall Wharf although it was highly inefficient as two men had to start work at 6 a.m. to get up steam and it burned a fortune in coal. About 1952 it was replaced by a handsome Rolls Royce diesel engine on top of a second hand loco chassis, our new toy costing £5,000[3].

When railway wagons were not returned promptly demurrage was charged, so they were always unloaded without delay. On one occasion a strike included the train drivers so the Traffic Manager Frank Cook, assisted by a trainee shipyard manager Charlie Gifford, hauled the wagons between Shieldhall and the Yard. Charlie drove the puggy and Frank did the more skilled job of shifting the points. Charlie eventually wanted a change so they swapped places. After several uneventful journeys they returned from the siding and were horrified to find a Glasgow Corporation tram full of passengers sitting in the middle of the Shipyard. Charlie had forgotten to reset the points on the previous journey and a tram, bowling along the straight stretch on Govan Road, had been suddenly precipitated through our back gate into the Yard. With no overhead power the tram and its astonished passengers were helplessly marooned and it was some time before the stranded vehicle could be pushed back onto its own rails.

In 1953 I was given my first job with a free hand to reorganise the road transport. We operated ten articulated and platform lorries and two vans to service the Shipyard, Engine Works and Repair Departments. In addition about 12 horses and carts were hired in. The cart drivers and their powerful Clydesdale horses worked hard but the system was inefficient. They moved material inside the works and collected rubbish, dumping it on our 'coup', the spare ground east of Holmfauld Road. Skips, as used today, were still in the future, so specially made containers were placed at strategic points throughout the works where they could be lifted and tipped into a lorry. We bought a 5 ton 'tipper' lorry with a specially fitted half ton crane, a crude affair compared with those used now, but it was

3. £137,000 today.

the second vehicle mounted crane in Scotland. After that one man collected and dumped all the rubbish in less than 20 hours a week, leaving the lorry free to help the Repair Department where their men often worked without cranage. The horses were phased out when our vehicle organisation was centralised and all vehicles were fitted with radio control. The lorry drivers were enthusiastic about their new radios but found it hard to understand that shipyard language was unacceptable on the air. Eight vehicles gave a greatly improved service and additional transport was hired to deal with peak demand. Our drivers were not unionised although John, one of our senior drivers and a rather dour man who had converted from horse to lorry, remained a member of the Scottish Horse and Motorman's Union. He was our sole member and his Union never caused us any trouble.

During the war we had used almost 5,000 tons of coal a year but by 1951 the usage was down to 3,200 tons. Steam cranes on rails were still in use because of the three year delivery time for mobile cranes. The blacksmiths' furnaces used 'cannel'[4] coal, the steam locomotive 'splint', heating boilers 'singles' or 'doubles' and the riveters used 'breeze', which was a coke suitable for their fires. Riveters wanted the best quality of breeze which came from Dumbarton gasworks and they sometimes rejected a wagonload. It was shovelled back into the wagon, left at Shieldhall siding for a day or two and brought in again with a different label. None was ever turned down a second time. All coal was unloaded from the wagons near the back gate by hand and later taken to its point of use by horse and cart. There was no easy way of getting the coal out of wagons other than by hand but an agricultural Ferguson tractor with a shovel and trailer was able to stockpile and distribute it. As soon as it became practical to get coal delivered by road to its point of use, the tractor became redundant.

4. A corruption of 'candle', coal from Muirkirk with a high gas content.

The two inefficient smithy furnaces showed an excessive usage of cannel coal because much of it was spirited away for illicit fires so they were replaced by one smaller electric furnace. The retiral of the steam locomotive reduced usage still further. The large central oil fired heating boiler gradually extended its operation to almost all buildings, getting rid of many individual coal boilers and their attendants. It was not many years before the only coal required was 'riveters' breeze' for the Repair Department who still had to deal with riveted ships. This usage was measured in bags rather than tons and soon the need for coal was at an end.

We were building our usual mix of ships at that time. The P & O group were, as always, our main customers. They included New Zealand Shipping Company, Federal Steam Navigation, whose handsome refrigerated ships ran between Britain and New Zealand, and the Union Steamship Company of New Zealand. We had a long and happy relationship with Rab Beattie, the Marine Superintendant for all these companies, who was a regular visitor to Linthouse. P & O presented us with an unusual problem for *Enton* and her later sister ships *Donegal* and *Antrim* in that they only decided which of their companies would own them at the last minute. For the first they decided on Birt, Potter & Hughes and the other two Avenue Shipping Company, both paper companies. At the last minute we had to topcoat the funnel in the required colours and paint the ship's name on the hull. Staging was rigged at bow and stern and one of these late alterations resulted in the death of Willie Milne our Loft Foreman, for whom I had worked briefly. Misfortune struck when he fell off the staging and was drowned. The only other fatality I recall during my time at Linthouse was during a lunch hour when two apprentices were doing an Errol Flynn type sword duel in the timber yard, where they should not have been. During their escapade a pile of timber suddenly collapsed and one young man was killed.

In the years after the war the delivery time for ships was up to three years and it was not possible to give accurate delivery dates or costs. All ships were built on 'cost plus' which was the 'cost plus an agreed percentage of profit'. Shipowners were making money as freight rates were high and they were desperate to get their ships with cost not being vital. However 'cost plus' bred bad habits as the shipbuilder had little incentive to be efficient and the shipowner was prone to order a higher standard than was necessary. We aimed for a profit of 5% but with hindsight we should have gone for a higher profit *and* made a greater attempt to reduce our costs.

In 1951 we delivered *Aureol*[5] to Elder Dempster. She was our second post war passenger ship, 13,000 tons carrying 329 passengers and 145 crew and powered by twin Doxford engines each of 4,000 horsepower. The building went smoothly and she became Elder Dempster's successful and much loved flagship and, in my opinion, the most elegant looking British passenger ship of her time. She ran between Britain and Lagos and always carried some passengers who chose to make the round trip as though she were a cruise ship. However as the colonies became independent, fewer people travelled to them and those who did, found it easier to travel by air and so *Aureol* had to be taken out of service in 1972. She was never put to really good use after that and was finally scrapped in 2001.

Every passenger ship at that time carried a substantial amount of cargo, but we built the first of a new breed, almost a 'passenger only' ship with minimal cargo space. John Goulandris had run cargo ships and one or two small second hand passenger ships but a purpose built passenger ship was new to him, and the 23,000 ton *Olympia*[6] was the only ship we built for Greek shipowners. She was originally conceived

5. Plates 8.
6. Plate 65.

to take emigrants across the Atlantic with cheap accommodation little better than a doss house, but as the design progressed the specification was upgraded for cruising in the off season. Her fitting out, always a major task on a passenger ship, was a highly planned operation. On the berth, as soon as the steelwork for a cabin block was finished, the fitting out trades moved in. As they completed each space, it was locked up and the tradesmen moved to the block above. Our insurance company insisted that sprinklers were operative in all completed spaces and sometimes they were working ahead of time. On one occasion when a minor alteration to some steelwork required riveting, a squad moved in and started up their fire. The sprinklers worked perfectly and the unsuspecting riveters got soaked.

Our joiners were fully stretched by the cabin accommodation on passenger ships so public rooms were always designed and fitted by outside contractors. On *Olympia* some public rooms were interesting, some tasteful and others somewhat startling. The designer of the dining saloon had no experience of ships and demanded that the steel pillars in the dining saloon be removed. It was explained to him that ships needed them to support the deck above, the only alternative being deep steel beams. He insisted on the beams until he realised that the passengers and crew would have to crawl to pass under them.

Olympia was delivered on time but, because of the changes in concept, there was a large bill for extras which were modestly priced and not designed to increase the profit which finished up at 3½%. Unfortunately John Goulandris Senior had taken ill and died just before the ship was launched and his place was taken by his son, also John. Young John had not been involved in the development of the ship and thought he was being overcharged. Deadlock was reached and my father refused to hand over the ship. Money was deposited in special bank accounts and the differences eventually thrashed out. It was the only occasion in my time where we had any serious disagreement with shipowners. The major bone of contention had been the heating system in the accommodation – only public rooms being air conditioned in those days. Goulandris had originally asked for the cheapest available system and had accepted that certain valves would be adjusted by hand to control the temperature. The engine room and deck crew were Greek and the stewards German but, due to their bitter enmity during the war, the two nations were still not on speaking terms. During the trials the engine room crew set the valves whereupon the stewards changed the settings and there was chaos. In spite of disagreements we got on well with the Goulandris team.

The brochure for *Olympia's* maiden voyage in November 1953 advertised accommodation for 138 first class passengers and 1150 tourist. There were 3 main lounges, 3 cocktail bars, 3 dining rooms, 2 libraries, a writing room, a card room, a drawing room, a picture gallery, 2 winter gardens, the 'New Pavilion', a two storey cinema, 2 swimming pools, 2 gyms, 2 children's rooms, an open air playpen, a solarium, 2 shops, 2 beauty parlours, 2 hairdressers, an enclosed promenade deck and ample space on other decks. The tourist fares to New York were from £60[7] for a berth in an inside cabin for 8 people to £70 for a double cabin. First class varied from £98 to £146 for a suite on A deck.

Goulandris Brothers ran *Olympia* successfully but after several changes of ownership she was refitted in 1990 and renamed. In 2003 she was bought for £1.1 million at a bankruptcy auction and replaced the ex Shaw Savill *Southern Cross* which was two years younger. *Olympia* was retired in 2007 and finally scrapped in 2009 having outlasted all her contemporaries.

During the year I worked in the Ship Drawing Office

7. £1,500 today.

Olympia was still at the design stage and I arranged cabin layouts in blocks of accommodation where my instructions were to fit in as many passengers as possible. It was a fascinating puzzle although on one occasion a really good layout was ruled out because there simply wasn't space for one door to open. After the ship had been launched I worked on board as a junior Fitting Out Manager and enjoyed seeing the plans I had drawn becoming reality. While she was being built, a second passenger ship was designed for Goulandris and even allocated a ship number. She would be a slightly smaller ship and a considerable improvement on *Olympia* with standard cabins and designed for cruising at reasonable cost. Before the war our *Viceroy of India* cruised during the off season but only the first class accommodation was occupied. Cruising had only been for the well heeled but John Goulandris senior realised it could be for the masses. Alas his son did not have the courage or vision to proceed and the contract was cancelled. Had Goulandris senior lived to a normal old age, this ship could have initiated the now enormous cruise industry and the history of Alexander Stephen & Sons might have been very different.

Some Greek shipowners had the reputation of being difficult and devious. In the mid 1950s my father was a member of the University Grants Committee which allocated Government money to British Universities for capital projects. On one occasion he came home from a tour spitting with rage at the dishonesty of the professors – "They have no conscience about lying to get what they want and are worse than the worst of Greek shipowners. The worst of the lot are the Welsh professors". A generation later my experience was similar with university research. As a director of Investment Trusts which put money up for research I found that, to further his career, one research fellow was quite happy to suppress the truth in ways the most unscrupulous ship operator would not have contemplated.

Another interesting and handsome ship was the car and

train ferry *Princess of Vancouver*[8] built in 1955 for the Canadian Pacific Steam Ship Company which was the successor to the Glasgow based Allan Line for whom Stephen's had built many ships. A year before we had received the order *Princess Victoria*, a similar car ferry which was not built by us, had foundered off Loch Ryan with considerable loss of life in a hurricane force gale. As a result the Ministry of Transport became over-cautious about the design and to satisfy them, we had to strengthen the bow doors and enlarge the scuppers on the vehicle deck. The Canadians were worried about fire so asbestos replaced the wooden bulkheads. Since then asbestos has been classified as one of the worst possible health hazards but to the best of my knowledge none of the joiners who fitted it or the crew who lived with it suffered from asbestosis. The car and train deck was similar to car decks in modern ships but steelwork was intricate because of the flush train rails. The *Princess* had the first modern style bow thruster. The original shipowner's sketch had an underwater propeller just aft of the forepeak. Nobody knew exactly what was expected and no conventional propeller maker was able to help. We eventually fitted a Voith Schneider propeller with vertical rotating paddles in a transverse rectangular slot and it worked well. Initially the ship operated between Nanaimo and Vancouver Island but later called at other ports in that area. In 1993 she was sold to Haveton Shipping Company of Hong Kong and was still in service in 2014.

Air travel was becoming cheaper and quicker, so the market for passenger ships, which had been our great strength, all but disappeared. The ships in demand best suited to our shipyard were refrigerated ships carrying 12 or 24 passengers. Hold insulation was becoming more specialised so, after our shipwrights had completed *Patonga* in 1953, all insulation work was subcontracted.

8. Plates 67 and 68.

I spent a relaxed but interesting year in the Ship Drawing Office and learned not to get upset when my carefully drawn plans came back from Lloyds Register of Shipping[9] covered in red ink. Draughtsmen considered themselves socially superior to the Shipyard production staff. The Drawing Office kept a private book full of press cuttings and poems with a large and amusing section about the Stephen Staff Canteen. Sadly I can remember only two lines, about Ferguson, a tough Ship Manager, promoted from the shop floor:

Then in came Big Fergie, a man of mighty bulk;
Sat down at the table, said "Will you'se pass up the mulk".

Drawing offices were springboards for promotion usually to Manager but for some to Lloyds Register. Others with less ambition were happy to remain draughtsmen all their lives and Willie Gavin was one of these. After lunch he always had a short snooze at his drawing board for which he had trained his pencil hand to keep moving. A livelier draughtsman, holding a sheet of paper between Willie's eyes and hand, would evoke no reaction.

In 1954 I married Sue Thomson, the great-grand-daughter of James Thomson who, with his brother George, became co-founders of J & G Thomson. As Engineers they set up Clyde Bank works near the present Exhibition Centre in Finnieston then in 1851 diversified into shipbuilding in Govan while continuing to use the name Clyde Bank. They were extremely successful but the brothers fell out. James returned to Engineering with his son and named his company J & J Thomson, building engines for Stephen's before we could build our own. George took the shipyard downriver to a greenfield site and took with him the name Clydebank. The company was bought

9. All our plans had to be approved by Lloyds Register of Shipping to allow the ship to be certified by them for insurance purposes.

over by John Brown in 1899 and went on to build many illustrious ships. Sue and I, both with ship building in our blood, have been happily united ever since.

CHAPTER 4

Demarcation Strikes

No occupation: all men idle – The Tempest
A plague on both your houses – Romeo & Juliet

The shipbuilding industry suffered from an unreasonable number of strikes. Confrontation between management and unions was nothing new. My great-great-great-grandfather William Stephen endured strikes of Aberdeen shipwrights over wage rates more than 200 years ago. In later years the confrontation continued and positions became entrenched. Trade Union rules, although democratic on the surface, favoured extremists. Shop stewards thus tended to be trouble makers, some going on to become Union officials. The Trade Unions, the Boilermakers' in particular, had achieved a dominant position and we had great difficulty in negotiating with them. Not until Margaret Thatcher had won her battle with the National Union of Mineworkers would this position change but by then it would be too late for shipbuilding.

The Unions were not wholly to blame for the position. In my younger days I came across some appallingly conservative managers in others yards whose attitudes made me cringe. There were many ways of getting loyalty from the workforce. I worked at Hamilton's of Port Glasgow under Horace Willson who was one of the best man managers I ever met. He was really tough with his men. If his welders banned overtime, they could expect to be offered no overtime for a similar period when they relaxed their ban. In his earlier days he was reputed to have reached an impasse with a shop steward and gone out to the stockyard to settle it by fisticuffs. He was universally respected because everybody knew exactly where they stood with him and he knew all his long service men together with their family circumstances.

In the 1950s there were 27 Trade Unions at Linthouse. On ships, several tradesmen often had to work in a small and cramped space, where give and take was essential so it was easy for a dissatisfied person to turn one of the many grey areas into a demarcation dispute. As every Union was set against losing work to any other, the officials tended to take a hard line and when a demarcation dispute escalated into a strike, management could rarely solve it. Differentials in wage rates were also a regular cause of friction. If the welders got an increase, the other trades within the Boilermakers' Union wanted one too, and, if they succeeded, the finishing trades all wanted more to maintain the differential. Opportunities for spreading discontent among the workforce were endless.

Relaxing after a difficult meeting between management and unions some years later I was chatting to a really worthy Painters' Union delegate with whom I had just had a serious barney when he confided "I agreed with what you said, Mr Stephen, but if I had said so, I would be voted out of office at our next election". All Union officials were in the same position. Not all boilermakers caused problems. Jimmy Fox, our highly effective Head Foreman Blacksmith was once asked "How is it that you never have any trouble? Who is your shop steward?" Jimmy's reply came in his delightfully gravelly voice "Ah'm the f•••••• shop steward". When not under pressure from their Union, the Linthouse labour force was both loyal and hardworking.

Historically the shipwrights, being craftsmen in wood, had resisted the introduction of iron for shipbuilding, as some even doubted that an iron ship would float, so boilermakers were brought in to do the work the shipwrights had rejected. Boilermakers then specialised, becoming platers, riveters, caulkers, burners, drillers, sheet iron workers, blacksmiths or welders.

The relationship between Shipwrights' and Boilermakers' Unions remained difficult, but relative peace reigned with riveted ships as the demarcation between the two Unions had been clearly agreed, but welding and the consequent prefabrication destroyed this peace. Shipwrights had erected frames and faired the ship's hull while boilermakers had done the rest. Large units were now put together in the fabrication bays and the interfaces between the two skills became completely different. The Shipwrights' Union wanted to keep their percentage of the work while the Boilermakers' wanted all of it.

In 1956 Alexander Stephen & Sons led the British shipyards in prefabrication. It was accepted that boilermakers did all the work in the fabrication bays but which Union was to erect the units on the berth was the problem. My Uncle John negotiated a Yard agreement and Combined Erection Teams with 60% platers and 40% shipwrights were formed. The two trades worked well together, but when other shipyards started along the same route, the boilermakers set about trying to oust the shipwrights. Their Union decided that the battle to achieve this should be fought out at Linthouse, the only yard committed to the new ways. Our boilermakers went on strike but were coaxed back whereupon the shipwrights, who felt they were in danger of getting a raw deal, went on strike. And so it continued. The shipwrights, although generally amenable, could strike just before a launch thereby postponing the operation for two weeks because ships could only be launched on spring tides. We were powerless to prevent a series of strikes and months of production were lost. 1958 was the worst year with the yard being almost completely closed for six months. At the 1958 Annual General Meeting my father summed up the position by saying "for some thirty years, up to a year ago we had been untroubled by strikes and had had excellent relations with our men and their union delegates. But with the changes involved in the modernising of our works, which have been going on for some years and are now virtually complete, at a cost of over £1 million[1], we have never been free from trouble with those sections of our men affected by these changes. We had expected the new lay-out to have given us a greater production on two scores, (1) by allowing us to employ more men, and (2) by a greater output per man due to the new facilities. On neither score have we had any benefit at all. Up to the moment we should have been better off if we had not spent a penny on the shipyard."

It was not just the Shipyard that suffered. The Engine Works was geared to shipyard production and was also reduced to a standstill. The Repair Department was unable to take on major jobs because the likelihood of a strike was ever present, and shipowners would not risk their ships with an organisation which walked out on strike half way through an urgent repair. The Company was brought to its knees financially and, had the strike gone on much longer, would have faced bankruptcy. It was not until April 1959 that the Unions eventually reached agreement and Combined Erection Teams were accepted with almost exactly the same ratio that Uncle John had agreed some years earlier. Work restarted but so much hate had been created that the friction between the two Unions was deeply embedded. Morale was at an all time low and it is my belief that our management never recovered their pioneering spirit and just accepted the inefficiencies of our labour system. We never made any progress to eliminate the lack of flexibility. To fit a porthole in a steel bulkhead a shipwright marked off the hole, then a driller pierced the steel for a caulker to cut the hole out, a shipwright marked the places for a driller to make bolt holes and finally the porthole was fitted by a shipwright. Efficiency could only have been achieved if the Boilermakers' and Shipwrights' Unions had merged and allowed the structure within the combined Union to be thought out afresh.

The dispute would have been a lot less devastating, but for

1. £25 million today.

one man, a Platers' shop steward who had not been with the Company for long and who led a thoroughly disruptive, vitriolic campaign causing trouble and hate at every turn. He seemed determined to ruin the Company and nobody in his Union at any level stood up to him. All steelworkers were laid off during the last of the many strikes and when work eventually restarted, it was carefully arranged that he was not re-employed. By this time the central management of the Boilermakers' Union had understood the damage that had been done and made no complaint. No other shipyard would touch him, but eventually the Boilermakers' District Delegate approached the Clyde Shipbuilders Association which dealt with labour matters on the river and asked that the Shop Steward should be given employment. Connell's[2] agreed to take him on but their shop stewards violently opposed his appointment and were not pacified until the background position was explained to them. It was no surprise therefore when Connell's declared him redundant after a few months but hinted that John Brown's might offer him a job. He was the object of 'pass the parcel' for several years and eventually, much to everyone's relief, the Shop Steward disappeared from the scene.

Throughout Britain there was widespread fear of 'Reds under the bed' with some industries convinced that communists could destroy the capitalist system. In the demarcation strikes at Linthouse there was no evidence of communist activity, merely bloody minded people; the disruptive Shop Steward was a Roman Catholic so could not have been a communist. Soon after the war Uncle John offered the post of Electrical Manager to John Byrne who was then the Electrical Trades

2. The first shipbuilding Charles Connell was a Manager at Linthouse before he branched out on his own account. 'Young' Alexander Stephen recorded the event in his diary saying 'I do not think he will succeed'. Later he added a footnote recording 'Charles Connell died this day leaving £300,000'.

Union official in charge of the West of Scotland. Byrne said that the offer greatly appealed to him as it would give him more money and greater stability than he could achieve in the Union, but he was one of the few people in the ETU who was fighting the communists and this had to be his life's work. This fine man continued the fight and eventually defeated the Reds but stress destroyed his health and he died at an early age.

Fortunately there were areas where the Unions did not trouble us at Linthouse. This book has already shown how we reduced the number of road transport operators from 24 to 8 giving a better service with no hint of labour problems. In 1954 I was given the remit of getting stores and stock under control. ICI in Birmingham kindly took me on for six weeks to learn about their stock control and buying methods. I set about finding out the situation in our own yard where stores, sub-stores, storemen and stock proliferated with no co-ordination between departments. There were 103 storemen and the stock was valued at £643,000 (£15,000,000 today) which figure included little steel as we had to work hand to mouth with plates and sections ordered to size for each ship.

Timber presented the biggest problem. The necessity of carrying large stocks resulted in our having a book value of £235,000. Shipwrights, on piecework naturally used up the long and straight lengths of teak decking, rejecting the short lengths and planks with blemishes. As the chance of building passenger ships receded, the supply situation eased so stock could be reduced although the shipwrights were at first unkeen to use up the large amount of less than perfect decking. Two magnificent teak logs had lain in the timber yard for years and were the pride and joy of the Timber Buyer. He was almost in tears when I told him to cut them up and use them which revealed two things: firstly that the Shipyard sawmill was seriously outdated and thereafter timber came into the Yard cut to size: secondly we no longer needed a specialised Timber Buyer who fortunately had just reached retiring age. A very competent foreman, John Black, could now run a much smaller show. Stock control of timber remained a problem because the percentage of waste varied enormously.

Throughout the Yard, shortages had been so severe that anything of possible use had been accepted and preserved resulting in unnecessary variety and a surprising number of items which no-one could identify. The Engine Shop Store had been run by 'Jock' during the war years. He had a photographic memory and when a delivery was made, he removed the label but remembered exactly where he had put the material. Unfortunately his memory deteriorated and he forgot where he had put things but claimed that they had never been delivered and the store became chaotic leaving an Aladdin's Cave after he retired. When I became involved in stock control, reordering and costing for the Engine Works was run by a qualified engineer, Walter MacGeorge, and two girls and I set up a similar organisation for the Shipyard under Bert Reid, an accountant, with five girls. Agreeing standards and descriptions throughout the Company wasn't easy. A hexagonal headed or 'hex head' screw was also called a 'setpin' or a 'setscrew' and warships needed different threads from everybody else. Most items were grossly overstocked. Odd sizes and types were gradually used up and surprisingly little was scrapped. Items made by our tradesmen were replaced by mass produced fittings often costing less than the material would cost us. The rivet store had been highly efficient in its heyday with a bogey on rails and large bins about thirty inches across with stocktaking done by volumetric calculation but I doubted the accuracy of this method and asked for the rivets in one bin to be bagged and weighed. After the top few inches had been removed from the bin a mass of rusty rivets was revealed, which had to be chipped out with a power hammer. The greatly reduced stock was eventually transferred to the General Store to be kept in bags and dispensed from a small ready use bin.

The delivery time for plumbers' steel pipes had been over

two years so we had placed many forward orders. Stewarts and Lloyds suddenly caught up on their deliveries and delivered it all in three months. Before we could tell them to stop we were inundated with pipes. The covered storage space was filled so the rest had to be left in the open. By the time the last of this deluge was needed, some pipes had rusted to such an extent that they could not be used on ships. For plumbers' material and fittings the old stable, the only building which had survived from the country estate of Linthouse, made a surprisingly effective store. Our Head Foreman Plumber was a genial man from the North of England with the appropriate name of Stan Plumb. I got to know all the Head Foremen well while working with them on the stock and found them both able and progressive.

Storemen were generally not in the first flush of youth, some having previously worked on ships and others being suited to a less physically demanding job. They were intelligent and co-operative and several had worked out their own systems of stock control. 'John', the smithy storeman, was a voracious reader, entirely self taught, who loved to ensnare me in philosophical discussion and referred to the "swor-r-d of Damoccles (to rhyme with cockles) hinging ower us". 'Andy', the Sheet Iron Department storeman, was a dour character. I spent twenty minutes extolling the advantages of stock control. He listened in total silence and at the end his only comment was "It'll no wur-r-k". The Paint Store, separate from other buildings because of the fire risk, was beside the road to Shieldhall Wharf, so hundreds passed it every day. Annie Hackson, 'Big Nan', was Assistant Paint Storeman for about forty years and the only female storeman in the Yard. She was a large and delightful lady and everybody's friend. My earliest encounter with her had been as a small boy making my first visit to Linthouse. I had got paint on my coat and was taken to her to get it removed. My last encounter with her was when she was a pensioner of the Stephen Bicentenary Trust and she still impressed everyone with her charm. Storemen belonged to various Trade Unions but were all treated equally and there was never any hint of labour trouble. Would that the same had applied in shipyard production.

The 'Aircraft Store' had been erected in 1916 for our joiners to build aeroplanes for the First World War but became redundant after a brief period of making wooden legs for wounded servicemen. Thereafter it was used to store light machinery and equipment which would go onto the ships, most of which was delivered in returnable wooden crates. Everything had to be manhandled as there was only an elderly electric one ton lifting block on a rail but the Electrical Department Store in the north end of the building already had a 5 ton gantry crane for handling cable drums which was then extended to cover the whole area. Entrance had been from Holmfauld Road which made for bad security but the lie of the land allowed a loading bay to be excavated inside the yard. The store's capacity was greatly increased and it could be run by two men instead of the previous eight.

When stores were amalgamated and repositioned, improved handling methods made huge savings. Welders' electrodes had been carried from the delivering lorry to the Welders' Store by eighteen apprentices who were kept away from their work for well over half an hour. In the new General Store which opened onto the Fabricating Bays the lorry driver fed the electrodes onto rollers and one storeman could put them into the bins in twenty minutes.

I was extremely lucky to have a totally reliable Stores Superintendant in Doug Falkingham who was an ex Royal Navy Stoker Petty Officer. If a storeman complained about a job being too hard Doug would take his jacket off and do it himself saying "If I can do it in twenty minutes, you can do it in forty". His loyal assistant, Alec Mackie, was responsible for the prompt return of empty crates and cable drums on which there were hefty deposits and was known throughout the Yard as the 'Minister for Empty Boxes'. When storemen reached retiring age they were not replaced and by 1963 the number had been reduced from 103 to 21 with little or no redundancy. The Shipyard and Engine Department stock control offices were amalgamated in due course and, with new systems, staff numbers were reduced from two men and seven girls to Walter MacGeorge and two girls. Stock was reduced to just under £100,000 by 1967, a 90% reduction over 13 years if inflation is taken into account.

Great-great-great-grandfather William Stephen used to preach to his shipyard workers in Aberdeen during their dinner hour. Sometimes he had not finished when the bell rang and the men began to move off obviously preferring work to being preached at. He would call them back saying "Na, na, lads, stay where you are; you're in my time now". The evangelistic spirit was no longer there in my time but all religions were treated alike. Protestants predominated but West Highlanders and the Irish swelled the Catholic numbers. Our Engine Works Boilershop was Protestant to a man, but the Outside Boiler-makers Department who installed what had been made in the shop, was Catholic. The two denominations worked in perfect harmony but if management had tried to alter the status quo, there would have been trouble. The office contained both religions. Joan MacLeod, a fervent Wee Free, who was latterly our Cashier, allocated jobs to the office boys. She asked them where they had been to school and if a saint was named they were given the least attractive work. She was reprimanded but similar happenings were hard to prevent.

Billy Connolly the actor served his apprenticeship as a welder with Stephen's after having been a pre-apprentice office boy where he was seconded to the Joiners' Store under Jimmy Bain, a man of few words. One day Jimmy took him to visit the air compressor operator who looked Billy up and down in complete silence and eventually said "Catholic". "He never gets it wrong" said Jimmy. A high powered business executive once told me that his father, an Irish Catholic, had started in John Brown's and realised that, as a Catholic, he would remain a labourer so he had changed his religion, joined the Masons and eventually became a head foreman.

The Saturday religion was football. Rangers was the local team with their ground a mile from Linthouse but there was strong Celtic support. Fans of both teams could behave like animals but their fervent support may have acted as a safety valve because the troubles of Northern Ireland never spilled over into Glasgow. I sometimes stood at the Shipyard main gate at starting time to see how promptly the men were coming in. On the Monday morning after a Rangers/Celtic match a man's religion could be deduced by a smile or a frown. All players of these two clubs were full time but Jackie Husband, one of our engine draughtsmen, played for Partick Thistle and Scotland. There were West Highlanders of both religions in the Yard and English was a second language to some. All cranes had to display their Safe Working Load but Highlanders preferred to think that 'SWL 10 Tons' meant 'She Will Lift 10 tons'. Not everyone took religion seriously like the non-believer who insisted he was a 'Protestant atheist'.

CHAPTER 5

The Lull Before the Storm, 1955–59

To-morrow, and to-morrow, and tomorrow,
Creeps in this petty pace from day to day – Macbeth

The demarcation dispute between the Boilermakers' and Shipwrights' Unions took centre stage for several years. There was a long order book and our customers were very sympathetic when the delivery dates of their ships were put back, but it was difficult to keep their trust. At the same time our traditional customers whose business had been with the Colonies were feeling the pinch. Their passenger market had already been lost to the aeroplane and less cargo space was required as the volume of trade decreased. Many cargo liners had carried 12 or 24 passengers but this had become uneconomic so the ships which were now being built required less fitting out work.

While our customers were mostly British we sought foreign orders. Between 1954 and 1956 we built three 4,400 ton ships, *Irma, Fernvalley and Crux*, for Bergen Steamship Company. We found them good customers although we had to learn how to deal with the shipbrokers who played a role of great importance in the Norwegian shipping industry. We supplied a guarantee engineer on each ship for six months as their engineers had limited diesel engine experience. Our foreman fitters, who knew the engines thoroughly, undertook this job. The ships ran smoothly but one Guarantee Engineer Jackie Wallace, being unused to the high fish content in the Norwegian diet, was heard to remark "Fush! After a week ma stomach wis goin' in and oot wi' the tide".

Elders & Fyffes' transported bananas from the West Indies

to Europe and were among our oldest customers. Their refrigerated ships with 24 passengers suited us well and we had also built for them *Golfito*, a 10,800 ton 200 passenger/cargo ship with a service speed of 18 knots. During her trials the main engine gearing started scuffing and the surfaces of the teeth were getting damaged. After the teeth were repaired the same thing happened again and our investigations continued for weeks. The precise cause was never discovered but the problem was solved by moving the centres of rotation slightly closer together. There seemed little engineering logic in this but it worked. The Owners were understanding and our relationship was undamaged. Our gear cutting had not been at fault but a policy decision was taken for all gear cutting to be subcontracted thereafter. This had happened before *Stephen of Linthouse* was published in 1950 but it was not mentioned because it might have discouraged customers. Now, revealing all upsets nobody.

Golfito was so successful that Elders & Fyffes soon placed an order with us for a sister ship *Camito*[1] which we delivered in 1956 without gearing problems. They were fine ships and ideal for our facilities. *Changuinola*[2], *Chirripo* and *Chicanoa*, sister ships of 6823 tons with 24 passengers, were to follow. These ships had to be fast to ensure that the bananas, which give off a lot of heat, got to the European market in prime condition. For this purpose an efficient hull form with a deep draft was required but these ships also had to navigate shallow rivers in the West Indies where a small draft was essential. The solution was worked out by David Watson, our Naval Architect, with an ingenious ballasting system which raised the stern of the ship in the river so that the propeller was half out of the water but when the ship was loaded and the ballasting altered, it was at a depth to drive the ship efficiently. Following the

1. Plate 9.
2. Plate 10.

success of these ships we received an order for a fourth – *Chuscal* in 1959. Sadly she was the last ship we built for these customers as their fleet was by then up-to-date with capacity to handle all their business.

Captain Moore was Elders & Fyffes' Marine Superintendent and later General Manager. He was a great ally and regular visitor to Linthouse, and I shared his view that bananas are at their best when black on the outside. When he visited Linthouse Captain Moore was always driven by Miss Steele, the excellent chauffeuse who usually drove my father. Once, going to a meeting in Glasgow he handed her his hat as he got out of the car saying "See if you can get me another like this". After the meeting he found two identical hats on the back seat. She was an expert shopper and knew where the most unlikely things could be bought. Miss Baird, the other chauffeuse, lived near Uncle John in Ayrshire and drove him daily to his work. When he retired and moved to Deeside, Miss Baird went too. Hughie MacMurtrie, the chauffeur, was an expert on the old railway companies of Glasgow and the West of Scotland so certain customers with a similar interest were quite offended if it was not Hughie who was there to meet them. To employ three uniformed chauffeurs was extravagant but the stream of visiting Superintendents called for good service. However when our loyal chauffeuses retired, they were not replaced and Angus MacDonald from the Main Office filled in as required.

In 1952 the Admiralty placed their first post-war order for the frigates *HMS Murray* and *HMS Palliser*. They were more sophisticated than wartime ships and the Admiralty had become obsessed with saving weight in order to obtain extra speed. Consequently the hull plating was only ¼" thick, making it difficult to avoid distortion in the plating work. An Admiralty Inspector examining a deck we had erected thought it looked like a ploughed field and was reputed to have said "The Stephen family were farmers. They should have stuck to it". We satisfied them in the end. During *Palliser's* trials I went into the chain locker while the ship was on her speed trials and found the hull plating vibrating alarmingly. These ships were later used during the Cod War and Icelandic trawlers discovered that they could easily dent them without any damage to themselves. After that steel plating on frigates was of a more sensible thickness.

Murray and *Palliser* were the last Royal Navy sister ships we built but there was always one frigate under construction thereafter which kept our technical team together. The timescale for a warship was different from that of a merchant vessel taking far longer at every stage due to the complexity, tightness of space and higher standards required. Technology was advancing fast and the Admiralty was determined to have up-to-date ships. At one time so many alterations were required that it looked as though the ship would never be completed. The Admiralty had a permanent staff of about fifteen at Linthouse. About a year before the launch, the ship's Engineers started to arrive and gradually the crew built up. The ship's Captain, the resident Naval Constructor and the Engineer Commander were the only overseers to lunch every day with the directors. The Royal Navy were valued customers and we were anxious to keep our name on the list of warship builders.

Admiralty bureaucracy was never absent so it helped when a sense of humour emerged. *Murray* was named after a famous frigate captain but the name was undoubtedly allocated for my father's benefit. It may also have been with tongue in cheek that they appointed Murray Scrimgeour as the assistant resident Naval Engineer. Naval Officers tended to make their homes near Portsmouth or Plymouth but Murray was a staunch Scot and when I moved to Ballindalloch near Balfron, he was both neighbour and friend as he had bought the Old Stables of the estate and lived there for over forty years.

Until the 1960s, warship orders were placed on a 'cost plus' basis though the Admiralty negotiated a fixed price half way through the contract. The most profitable warship we built after the war was *HMS Zulu*[3] delivered in 1964. As the two previous negotiations had worked against us, we had achieved substantially less than the expected 5%', I was instructed to ensure that we did better with *Zulu* and the estimating team, Hugh Kemp in particular, did a great job and a price was agreed which eventually gave us 9% profit. The Admiralty considered this to be excessive and asked for a refund but when we suggested that the two previous warships should be taken into account they reluctantly agreed. *Zulu* would become the last ship in the Royal Navy to fire a broadside. When she was eventually sold to the Indonesian Navy, British warships only had one gun, albeit quick firing, so broadsides were not possible.

Two frigates were built for foreign navies, *Kirpan* for India and *President Steyn* for South Africa. The British Admiralty supervised the work but the foreign navies built up their own crews for the trials. We got on well with both nationalities and found that some of the Indian Navy officers spoke impeccable English and appeared even more RN than the RN. In the 1960s the Government reorganised Britain's fighting forces and the Admiralty became part of the Ministry of Defence or MOD. The reorganisation did not affect us but 'MOD' somehow sounded inferior and our workforce who had proudly referred to the 'Admirality' regretted the change. Technology confounded the English language when warheads replaced shells and the MOD issued the following instruction: "It is necessary for technical reasons that these warheads should be stored with the top at the bottom and the bottom at the top. In order that there may be no doubt as to which is the top and which is the bottom for storage purposes it will be seen that the bottom of each warhead has been clearly labelled 'Top'".

A friendly contact continued between our staff and

3. Plate 14. *Zulu* was the second Tribal Class destroyer of this name to be built at Linthouse, the first being delivered in 1938 only to be sunk in 1941 while supporting Allied troops in the beleaguered fortress of Tobruk in Libya.

warship crews who were often at Linthouse for some time. When *HMS Kenya* was commissioned in 1940 there was a wardroom party to which Sanny Brown, the Ship Manager, was invited. He was a great character and a tower of strength but on this occasion he went home somewhat intoxicated having been surreptitiously relieved of his customary bowler hat. For several years the bowler hung on a bulkhead in *Kenya's* wardroom and any officer who celebrated a birthday was invited to wear it and walk the quarterdeck. Some years later when the ship returned to the Clyde with the hat somewhat worse for wear, a replacement was needed so a party was organised for Stephen's staff. Needless to say Sanny was present and went home a second time minus his bowler hat.

In September 1958 *Waikari* was delivered to the Union Steamship Company of New Zealand whose business was coastal work round New Zealand and the east coast of Australia. They were part of the P & O Group but were managed from New Zealand. She was the thirteenth ship delivered to these owners over 11 years, all built to the same lines plan and with identical Sulzer engines. The internal arrangement in each ship was adapted to deal with anything from refrigerated cargo to bulk carriage, and their tonnage varied between 3510 and 3839. After we had built six ships for them, we offered to design a more efficient hull but they were satisfied with the existing design. *Waikari*, which completed their modernisation programme, was the last ship we built for them. Our link with Blue Star was renewed when we built *Chatham*, a small refrigerated ship of 3000 tons, in 1959. We were still building for the Ellerman Line and plate 12 shows the handsome *City of Melbourne*.

The tanker market was large and expanding very fast, so we hoped that it would be another string to our bow. The ratio of steelwork to fitting out was higher than suited our organisation but at that stage we were still intending to increase our steel output. The first two we built were *British Fulmar* and

British Curlew, product carriers for BP Tanker Co. The ships were a success but the main engines caused problems. They were Sulzer 7 cylinder engines with a rather large propeller which was not a good match. Our Engineers sometimes referred to these tankers as the 'dirty birds'. *Mobil Acme* and *Mobil Apex* which followed caused less trouble. They were built for Mobil Tanker Company so we had to adopt American standards for much of the equipment. They were turbine driven when other merchant ships of this size had moved on to the more efficient diesel engines.

The largest ship ever built at Linthouse was the crude oil carrying tanker *British Bombardier*[4] which at 50,000 tons deadweight was as large as we could launch. Because of her 725 foot length the declivity, the slope of the building berth normally 2.4°, was reduced to 1.8°. With a beam of 97 feet she was built diagonally across No. 3 and 4 berths to improve the launching angle into the river. Even with the reduced declivity the bow towered above Holmfauld Road and the berth at Shieldhall Wharf had to be dredged to avoid her grounding at low tide. Tankers were the only aft engined ships we built and our main fitting out crane was in a fixed position and not ideally sited on the wharf for installing their engines. All the tankers we built were profitable but our organisation was not at its best building these large steel boxes. By the time *Bombardier* was launched, tankers of over 100,000 tons were being constructed and the Japanese were building at prices we could not match. We had accepted our first tanker order hoping to be able to put through a greater tonnage of steel but, five years later, we had been unable to increase our steel output as we might have done, primarily due to the lack of welders, but also the restrictive attitude of all steel workers. Thus tankers, which had relatively little fitting out work, were not a good option for us and, though we quoted for some others, *Bombardier* was our last tanker.

4. Plate 13.

In the 1920s we had started building diesel main engines under licence from Doxford whose engine works was on the Tyne and we had also taken out a licence from Sulzer of Winterthur, Switzerland. Before the war, Doxford engines were almost universal but by the 1950s faster and larger ships needed more powerful engines. The opposed piston Doxford engine became less suitable and soon we were building nothing but Sulzers which were conventional and well engineered diesel engines. We had an excellent relationship with the company but we were only one of several British licensees. John D'Arcy's interest was on the technical side rather than production and he investigated new products for the Engine Works. British marine engine builders and the power station industry had set up Pametrada (Parsons and Marine Turbine Research and Development Association) many years earlier to design all their turbines. After World War II the two technologies separated as power stations became larger so Pametrada now designed only marine turbines. All the turbines we had built were to their design, but D'Arcy fancied De Laval of Sweden and had a long flirtation with them but we never came anywhere near getting an order. With hindsight this was not surprising as larger and more efficient diesel engines were rapidly replacing turbines. Although steam turbines still powered warships even they were soon to be replaced by gas turbines and diesels.

Another costly ploy was investigating the Free Piston Gasifier, a revolutionary system for ships' propulsion. Gasifier units, each with two opposed horizontally acting pistons, fed hot compressed gas into a turbine which drove the propeller shaft. We built a sample Gasifier which worked well but never got an order for a complete installation. J & J Denholm[5] installed this type of machinery in one of their ships but it was

5. My sister Liz married Ian Denholm, later Sir Ian and Chairman of Denholm's. Stephen's was never in the market for Denholm ships because they were bulk carriers and tramps.

not a success and the idea died. Although gasifiers had proved to be uncompetitive, we had a good spin-off with a two year contract from Castrol to help research lubricating oils. The small Gasifier test house had been built away from the main works to avoid possible noise, but the inhabitants of the houses on Govan Road complained of vibration transmitted through the ground so we ran the machine only during the day time. Other diversifications for the Engine Works were considered but none got very far.

The rolls in traditional steel works plate mills bent under pressure causing steel plates to be thicker in the middle. Lloyds and other classification societies, who specified the thickness of each plate, measured the thickness at the edge of the plate, so with steel companies charging by weight, we had to pay for steel we did not want and ships had to carry unnecessary tons of steel. In 1954 the steel delivery position began to ease and Consett Steelworks offered the services of their new '4 high steel plate rolling mill' whose rolls were backed up in the centre so that plates of uniform thickness could be produced. The new technology could also roll wider plates and virtually none were laminated, a defect all too common in the past. Almost all of our plate business was transferred to Consett and I had to visit Colvilles' Managing Director, Tom Craig, to tell him that they were going to lose a lot of our business. He was really nice about it and merely asked that Colvilles should have the opportunity to supply us once more when their own 4 high mill came into production. The Craig and Stephen families had known each other for a long time and Tom then lived in Invergare at Rhu which had once been my grandfather Fred Stephen's family home. Colvilles eventually installed their mill and regained most of our business but Consett did us a good turn. At Linthouse a shot blasting machine for steel plates and sections was installed and the pickling tank which had previously removed the surface scale became redundant. Steel was now on a production line for shot blasting and priming as it went into the Platers' Shed. Oxy-acetylene cutting technology improved although computer control was still in the future. Hereafter our effort went in getting the most out of what we had.

Glasgow's tram system had been replaced by buses, leaving our electric puggy the sole user of the tramlines between our back gate and Shieldhall railway siding. When the Corporation informed us that the ex-tramlines required repair at a cost of £16,000 we decided to investigate the economics of rail deliveries. There was a small extra cost for steel to be delivered by road but almost everything else came that way just as cheaply, so rail deliveries were abandoned and the puggy and its two operators were retired. Our Rolls Royce locomotive was still required to take engines, boilers and funnels from the shops to Shieldhall Wharf.

Having a joinery department was a great luxury. Office furniture could be made to order and bulkheads in the offices were easily altered but these one-off operations were expensive so 'open plan' was adopted in the Main Office. With mass produced metal and glass partitions, desks could be moved around in the open spaces and the 50 year old office became lighter and compared favourably with the newer Shipyard Office. Directors and senior staff could sometimes order joinery items to be made in the Shipyard but at their own expense.

Under my father's chairmanship there were few board meetings. He kept in touch with the other Directors individually so the board tended to meet only to take major decisions. Every morning all important papers were put on the boardroom table to be read and initialled by the Directors. There was often useful talk over lunch and the system worked surprisingly well. Annual General Meetings were usually a formality attended by employees and members of the family but outside shareholders attended from time to time. The Press was always in attendance and given a handout to be printed in the papers the following day and my father would refer to it briefly. The Auditors' report sometimes took up most of the time. The shortest AGM only lasted for one minute thirty seconds although the Chairman would have preferred it to be taken 'as read'.

Road traffic bottlenecks at the ferries and bridges over the Clyde were getting worse so Glasgow Corporation decided that a tunnel must be built on our ground immediately east of Holmfauld Road. The approach roads would swallow 2½ acres next to Govan Road but we had no plans for this area which was let out for allotments. The rest of the ground east of Holmfauld Road we had reserved for a fitting out basin in case our lease of Shieldhall Wharf from the Clyde Port Authority was not renewed. A tunnel would preclude this option but we were able to negotiate suitable guarantees on the wharf's tenancy. The tunnel operation was not to our advantage but objecting would merely delay a sensible development so we accepted the best terms available. Work started in 1959 and 60 foot steel piles were driven, some only twenty feet from my office windows. The noise was so deafening at one time that the only way I could use my telephone was to crouch in the kneehole of my desk and then extricate myself in a somewhat undignified manner when a visitor came into my office. On each side of the river, tunnelling shields moved slowly towards each other as cast iron linings were put in place behind them to form watertight tubes. Some years earlier we had discovered that the terrain was unstable when we installed a large lathe in the Machine Shop, 500 yards from the river, which refused to cut accurately. Eventually some bright spark noticed that the inaccuracy peaked twice a day coinciding with the tides and the problem was solved by installing deep foundations under the lathe.

One evening when I was working late on a tender there was a crash as a pane of glass in my window suddenly shattered. I removed the important papers to a safer place and looked out. One tube of the tunnel had blown out opposite my office window and huge lumps of earth and stones were being tossed high into the air. I telephoned the gatehouse to be told that the contractors were already in action. When the eruption stopped, my car which was under cover, had been enveloped in a thick coating of sand. I was lucky because the neighbouring car had had its roof stove in by a great clod of earth which came straight through the roof. I was told later that blowouts were quite common in tunnelling. The Clyde Tunnel was opened by Her Majesty the Queen in 1963, the first visit to Linthouse by a reigning monarch since George VI and Queen Elizabeth toured the Yard in 1940 to boost wartime morale.

The tunnel improved the flow of traffic enormously and Linthouse became more central with the Repair Department able to save a lot of time on voyage repairs. Holmfauld Road between the main gate and the river reverted to us but we never found a use for it. I used the tunnel frequently but missed the old fashioned ferries. Subsidence due to the tunnelling caused our Main Office to tilt four inches but the cracks which appeared were satisfactorily repaired. Constructed by Melville, Dundas and Whitson[6] in 1916, it had withstood a traumatic experience.

Uncle John Stephen retired on his 65th birthday in May 1959. He had not expected to become a shipbuilder as his elder brother Murray and twin brother Jim were the two lined up to serve the Company but after Jim was killed in World War I, John was called in. He was a good manager and had a good relationship with the labour force and Trade Unions. A great innovator, he invented the Cold Frame Bender which did

6. My brother Jim's daughter Irene is married to Roy Whitson of that Company. Once when Roy's grandfather noticed an idle man on a site and asked him what company he worked for, he was told "Melville, Dundas and some other b••••••r". He replied "I am the other b••••••r and you're fired". The Stephen office is shown in plate 6.

away with the furnaces in which frames had been previously heated to be bent to shape. This principle is now standard in almost every shipyard in the world. He was active and always seeking improvements which applied to his leisure time as well. John designed and helmed International 6 Metre Class yachts, winning the Seawanhaka Cup, the world championship for smaller keel boats, then left the sea to become a keen and innovative farmer. He finally retired to Deeside hoping for many happy years fishing, one of many sports at which he excelled, but his health deteriorated due to having been gassed in World War I and he died in 1970. In 2005 his son David was at the funeral of a shipbuilding colleague when a stranger sitting next to him asked "Are you a son of John Stephen?" and continued "Well, you won't know me as I was in Yarrow's shipyard all my life, but when I was an apprentice your father caught me poaching salmon on the River Findhorn and then invited me to fish". That was Uncle John all over.

KB Robinson having served the Company successfully for seven years took over as Shipyard Director, but soon found our horrific labour problems were getting on top of him and resigned after a few months. Uncle John came out of retirement to help appoint a successor. We were fortunate to have the right man 'in house' in Norrie McCrae, who was number two in the Repair Department. He was appointed Shipyard Director and, already knowing everybody he had to deal with, was able to slot into the job straight away and apply his steady hand. Norman Easton continued to improve the way the office was run but he was something of an unguided missile. In 1959 without consultation he wrote a letter to *The Times* criticising the shipbuilding industry. What he said was true but it should not have been written by anyone in his position. I suspect that my father, knowing Norman's good points, would have forgiven him, but the outcry from other shipbuilders meant that Norman had to go. He was replaced as Financial Director and Secretary by Humphrey Massey who had been with Blackburn Aircraft in Dumbarton and he carried on modernising our accounting and instituted more effective Board procedures.

On the other side of the world the Japanese were steadily building up their shipyards with an efficiency which would leave us miles behind. We still had a reasonable order book but it was getting shorter.

CHAPTER 6

Launches

Talkest thou nothing but of ladies? – Twelfth Night

"I name this ship .... May God bless her and all who sail in her". These words must have rung out almost a thousand times in the history of Alexander Stephen & Sons. The launch is the big event in the building of a ship. It is spectacular, exciting and not without risk when a towering mass of metal is suddenly transformed to become a vibrant entity in less than a minute. Even forty-six years after the last launch at Linthouse, the thought of thousands of tons of steel gliding down the ways sends a shiver of mixed anxiety and pleasure down my spine. Every launch at Linthouse was an occasion where wives, children, friends and relations of all employees were welcomed. Anyone could leave his or her place of work to enjoy the event so the ground at the head of the berth became crowded while adjacent ships and stacked units waiting to be erected were thronged. A happy atmosphere pervaded so whenever a pretty girl ascended the decorated platform, a chorus of wolf whistles could be expected. Draughtsmen would often find an excuse to leave their drawing boards to check a measurement on an adjoining ship and on their return the older draughtsmen who had witnessed countless launches still wanted to know all the details. Everybody returned to their work uplifted and fired by an overwhelming sense of pride.

While a successful launch was a joy, there was much that could go wrong and I never saw a perfect launch. Traditional methods, which had worked for centuries, changed very slowly and timber launching ways, rammed up under the hull, still gave the best results. A case in point concerned the grease used between the standing and moving ways. Animal grease in the form of tallow had been used for centuries, although in tropical countries squashed bananas were said to be equally good. When mineral grease was produced specially for launch ways, shipbuilders were reluctant to use it because they knew that the tried method worked and any savings the new material might yield were small compared with the possible risk of disaster. Knowing that Uncle John Stephen was an innovative shipbuilder, manufacturers offered a mineral based grease to Linthouse. When it was used on *HMS Cheviot* in February 1942, the ship stuck on the ways because the grease had been tested in the summer and was not suitable for lower temperatures. The ship had to be shored up again and the ways removed, but when modified grease was applied, the vessel was launched successfully at the next spring tide.

At Linthouse the River Clyde flowed west-nor'west, bending conveniently to give our berths a longer run downstream. Launches always took place at high water so shortly before the expected time shipwrights split out the wooden hull supports, transferring the weight of the hull onto the launch ways where steel 'daggers', usually two each side, stopped the ship from moving. A senior shipwright threw cubes of wood into the river at intervals and when they stopped moving upstream the critical moment had arrived because a river starts to ebb in midstream while still flooding at the edge. The locking pins on the daggers were removed and handed to the youngest apprentice shipwright who ran to the bow of the ship and held them up to be seen by the Shipyard Director on the platform. The launching handle was then unlocked and the lady launching the ship, who is formally known as the 'sponsor', was asked to pull the handle, causing the daggers to drop and the launching bottle to strike the bow. At Linthouse the bottle was held horizontally in a device of Uncle

John's design shown in plates 19 and 20 so that, when the lever was pulled, it instantly smashed against the ship. The failure of a bottle to break might bring bad luck to the ship so no chances were taken. The Admiralty could not accept anything French so champagne was a non-starter and 'Empire Wine' became our standard. As soon as the ship became waterborne the drag chains came into operation and huge piles of rusty chains, attached to the ship by long cables roared down the berth bringing the ship to a halt. Sometimes an apprentice presented the sponsor with a bouquet and found the compliment returned with a flower for his buttonhole.

At Linthouse the rise and fall of the tide was about ten feet at neap tides and sixteen at springs so launches took place within forty-eight hours of springs on a day when high tide avoided an antisocial hour. A southerly gale or heavy rain would sometimes cause an exceptionally high tide, but nature could also work in the opposite direction. When the *Viceroy of India* was launched in 1929 Uncle John, who was the Shipyard Director, had to report to his father Fred on the platform that the tide was six feet short of normal – something unheard of before or since. The ship's bow would certainly ground, but Fred told John 'Launch her – I will take the responsibility'. Lord Inchcape the P & O Chairman overheard the exchange and was rather scathing about our 'little' river but when the ship was drydocked only one or two plates had to be replaced.

During my time at Linthouse there were no launch accidents and few incidents. My worst moment was at the launch of *British Bombardier*, the 50,000 ton tanker. She was the biggest and heaviest ship we had ever launched. Labour troubles had delayed the launch and the greased ways had been in position longer than we would have liked. Our ships normally set off down the ways at a spanking rate but on this occasion nothing seemed to happen. Though I envisaged an appalling situation, I was reassured to see Norrie McCrae, the Shipyard Director, standing on the platform close to the bow, looking as though he hadn't a care in the world. After the longest 15 seconds of my life, movement was detectable and then the huge bulk slowly accelerated to gather speed just like any other ship. Norrie had set up a piece of wood to touch the bow and had been able to detect movement not apparent to those at the back of the platform. As the ship hit the water the worry transferred to David Watson who, as Naval Architect, had specified the weight of each bundle of drag chains, its position at the head of the berth, the length of each cable and where it was to be attached to the vessel. So that ships came to rest facing up and down the river, drag chains were attached to the starboard side. There were normally five bundles of chains but *Bombardier* required seven, two having been borrowed from Fairfield's next door. This ship had one bundle attached near the bow to slow her up before she was fully in the water. After the launch, measurements revealed that every bundle had finished within twelve inches of the calculated position. That evening after the huge tanker was safely tied up at the newly dredged Shieldhall Wharf everyone was happy and relieved.

Bombardier's launch was the most prestigious of my time. Lord Heathcoat-Amery, Chancellor of the Exchequer, was the principal guest, but as he was a bachelor, the sponsor that day was the wife of his brother Sir John Heathcoat-Amery, Bart. Lady Heathcoat-Amery performed her duties charmingly but after the launch when all the other arrangements had gone perfectly we were caught out in a most unusual way. She had chosen a bracelet as a launch gift but when she tried it on it was too small to go round her wrist. In former years, as Joyce Wethered, she had been a famous golfer and Gene Sarazen claimed that she was the best golfer of his time, male or female, putting it down to her powerful grip. The golfer's iron wrists were too big for the bracelet which had to be taken back to the jeweller and jumboised.

A gale force wind could enforce the postponement of a launch, but a stiff breeze had to be accepted. Warships, which were particularly light, could be blown about dangerously and one paid an unscheduled visit to Barclay Curle's shipyard on the opposite side of the river. Two tugs[1] normally waited in the river to pass hawsers up to the bow and stern of the ship but were often slow in connecting up so I was instructed to find ways to improve the situation. Having studied the problem from the land I concluded that the tugs should position themselves nearer where the ship was expected to stop. At the next launch I was on board one of the tugs and was tempted to jump overboard to escape the huge mass of metal looming overhead which thundered almost straight at us; so the solution had to lie elsewhere. The problem was solved eventually by using spring loaded guns on the ship to fire lines over the tugs. The hawsers were then tied onto the lines for the men on the ship to haul up and attach to bollards. I was not permitted to be on a ship during a launch as, since the launching disaster of the *Daphne*[2] a century earlier, the number was restricted to those with essential duties.

The launch guests were entertained in the Directors' Lunch Room overlooked by the half block models of earlier ships which decorated the oak panelled walls. On average there were about 60 people at the party of whom a third were Stephen Directors and Staff, and their wives, but 100 could be accommodated at a pinch. The programme was dictated by the tide and lunch or tea was served before or after the launch, but speeches were always made after the ship was safely in the water. The Stephen chairman was expected to complain about something for the press to print – shortage of steel, government policy or lack of it etc. The visiting shipowner would reply also making *his* points of complaint – low freight rates, late deliv-

1. Stephen's always employed Clyde Shipping Company tugs rather than Steel & Bennie's probably because they were potential customers and possibly because of the family connection.
2. This tragic accident is recorded in Chapter 17.

eries of ships etc. The sponsor merely pulled a handle and blessed the ship but when she was formally thanked, it had to be implied that the success of the launch had been entirely due to her. The vote of thanks fell in turn to the junior Stephen Directors. The sponsor usually replied but sometimes her husband responded for her.

I worked very hard on my first speech but when I had to make a second one I had used up my best material and thereafter my speeches were rather pedestrian. Only one draft script has survived. The vessel being launched on 19 April 1966 was the *Royal Fleet Auxiliary Sir Galahad* and the sponsor was the wife of General Sir Charles Richardson.

> "The pleasant duty which I have to perform today is to thank Lady Richardson for launching *Sir Galahad* so beautifully. Our records, as far they exist, show that this is the first time in the Firm's history that a General's wife has launched one of our ships. We have been graced by the wives of forty or fifty foreigners, myriads of merchantman, armfuls of admirals and scores of civil servants. We have even had a ship launched by an Emperor – the Emperor of Brazil. We cannot claim an RAF launch although we used to build aeroplanes in World War I. I am not familiar with Air Force habits to know if they find an excuse for a party as an aircraft comes into being, but as those which we made were packed into crates, we must assume that no celebration took place.
>
> This occasion is therefore a 'first' for us and we are lucky that it has been made memorable by Lady Richardson. She showed no anxiety and though the sea is not a soldier's natural element, she performed her duty in a graceful and charming manner. Lady Richardson already has a son and a daughter and now she has added a second daughter to her family. How she will

> deal with the problem of having a daughter who is also a knight, we must leave her to sort out, but I do not see how *Sir Galahad* can fail to have a highly successful career after being given such a splendid start".

Nobody dreamt of the tragic end that lay ahead of this gallant ship in the Falklands Islands, sixteen years later.

The Director who thanked the sponsor also presented her with the cork of the launching bottle and the red, white and blue ribbons which decorated it. By that time the ribbons had become a rather nasty soggy mass and we always wondered what the lady did with them. The bottle was always beautifully dressed by Miss Steele, for many years my father's faithful secretary, and even after she retired she continued to do this task. Her father John Steele had been our Head Foreman Patternmaker and, as a young man, had played for Rangers Football Club on Saturday afternoons. He was paid £1 if they lost, £2 if they won and £3 when they won a cup. Many years after she had retired, Miss Steele, 'Tibbie' to her friends but always Miss Steele to me, asked me to find a good home for the gold medal which had been presented to her father when Rangers won the Glasgow Cup of 1893–4. I wrote to Sir David Murray the Chairman of Rangers offering it to their museum but in spite of a reminder I received no reply, so I was not surprised when Rangers got into deep financial trouble under his Chairmanship. Miss Steele also suggested the Scottish Maritime Museum of which I was then a Trustee. They had no links with Rangers but everybody was happy when the medal was auctioned in 1997 and a cheque for £431.90 was sent to the Museum. I hope somebody treasures that medal.

The sponsor was chosen by the shipowner but the shipbuilder provided the gift for her to commemorate the launch, so the lady was consulted as to her preference and a brooch was often requested. Before the launch she would be taken into the Chairman's office to select from 3 or 4 items the one with which she would be formally presented. If it was a piece of jewellery it was later passed round the room for everybody to drool over. Occasionally furniture was requested and a Georgian walnut sewing table[3] was chosen at the launch of *HMS Dunkirk* in 1944 by Lady Ramsay, widow of Admiral Ramsay who, after Winston Churchill, arguably did more to win World War II than anybody else, brilliantly masterminding the evacuation from Dunkirk, the North African landings and the landings on D-Day. My father knew Ramsay when he was Controller of the Navy and thought the world of him. The table now belongs to his granddaughter Rowena, who is my wife Sue's cousin. Sue regretted that she never had the opportunity to launch a ship at Linthouse because she would have been glad to speak up for the shipbuilders' wives and the invisible support they gave to the Industry. Jim's wife Betty launched *Karanja* in 1948 when Lady Inchcape was unable to attend.

Launches gave a Shipowner an opportunity to entertain his customers, colleagues, contacts, friends, staff and their wives. Visitors usually arrived at the Central Hotel off the night sleeper from London, breakfasted and were entertained by the shipbuilder for the part of the day when the launch was not taking place. The programme varied according to the time of high tide and a trip round Loch Lomond by bus and boat was the most favoured outing. Stephen Directors and their wives acted as hosts and the junior member of the Stephen family acted as tour guide, a position I occupied for several years. At big launch parties, guests and hosts were issued with different coloured name badges which helped a host to avoid wishing a fellow Glaswegian who he had not previously met 'a pleasant journey back to London'.

All warships and some merchant ships were blessed by a man of God in a short but moving service on the platform and

3. Plate 66.

invariably included the hymn “For those in peril on the sea”. The Royal Navy usually provided a padre but the Linthouse Parish minister also obliged. His church had been built in 1900 with considerable help from Old John Stephen and the link with the Company was always preserved. Linthouse had originally been in the Parish of Govan whose Minister for many years was the Reverend Sir George Macleod, Bart. Macleod did a wonderful job in restoring Iona Abbey, but he and my father did not get on. They had been at school together and had lived not far apart but my father referred to him as ‘that damned socialist’. I met him only in his old age. He had served as Honorary Padre to the Mudhook Yacht Club, and accepted an invitation to the annual dinner when I was Admiral of the Club. The Reverend Sir George showed up as a tremendous character holding very strong opinions.

“I name this ship Six Three Six ...” was proclaimed by the young and beautiful Miss Goulandris as she pulled the lever for the ship as yet unnamed but identified by her yard number. The owners had approached the Greek Government hoping to get special tax conditions for the passenger ship, in which case she would be registered in Greece and called *Queen Frederika*. The matter was still under negotiation at the time of the launch and the Greek Government eventually refused the owners’ request so the ship was named *Olympia* and registered in Liberia. Linthouse had missed the chance of a Greek Royal visit.

An unusual problem was presented by *INS Kirpan* which we built for the Indian Navy in 1959. John Cowie, the Shipyard Buyer, was surprised to receive a purchase requisition from the Foreman Shipwright for 24 coconuts because the specification required the ship to be launched with a coconut rather than the usual bottle. Extensive research revealed that a coconut with the shell cut round its equator and twice through its poles broke satisfactorily in our machine. At the launch the coconut broke perfectly but as a precaution a box of doctored coconuts was placed nearby, just in case the platform party was required to pelt the retreating ship. I have no recollection of the Hindu version of "... May God bless her and all who sail in her".

We had to be on guard against the unexpected. Mobiloil was the parent company of Mobil Tanker Company who regarded their tankers much as we regarded our lorry fleet. The Tanker Company management invited the wife of one of the parent company bigwigs to launch the ship and couldn't object when she started laying down conditions. Their Resident Superintendant Engineer at Linthouse, a large and amiable man by the name of Gruber, came to Norman Easton in a frightful state to tell him that the lady was a rabid teetotaller and refused to launch the ship with a bottle containing alcohol. Gruber was worried that a deviation from tradition would cause a strike in the Shipyard, but was reassured when Norman came up with the idea that, as the ship's name was *Mobil Apex* the bottle should be filled with spring water from Ben Nevis, the highest mountain in Scotland. For those concerned about the alcoholic aspect, the spring would be one that flowed down to the famous distillery at the foot of the mountain. Everybody was happy but the lady was never told the whole story. I had to make the speech thanking her and sat next to her, finding that she was one of the dullest people I have ever met with absolutely no sense of humour.

The tin dredger *Banka* was built in 1963 for the Central Management Board of Indonesia whose Chairman was a General. We were told that his wife would launch the vessel but then discovered that he had three. While we were still scratching our heads on protocol, we learned that the sponsor would be his number one wife and that the other two would remain at home. The Indonesian party stayed in the Central Hotel and we arranged the rooms for them as usual. The only lady without a husband was put on the floor below the the General's suite and it was only after they were installed that it was discovered that she was the General's mistress, so a quick rearrangement had to take place. It was noticeable that the number one wife was in charge of the party when the General was not there and the mistress did exactly what she was told. The Indonesian wives looked graceful in their sarongs and made the European ladies look dowdy and almost elephantine.

At the launch of one dredger, the shipowners were headed by a knight and the vessel launched by a lady we assumed to be his wife. Only after the speeches did we discover the the sponsor had established her position by changing her Christian name to 'Lady'. Luckily we had avoided what could have been an embarrassing gaffe.

Shipowners often hosted a dinner party in the Central Hotel before leaving for London on the late sleeper train. The Stephen Directors and their wives were glad to be invited but we were always thankful to get to our beds after the long and stressful day.

CHAPTER 7

The Engine Works and Diversification

Once more into the breach – Henry V

Stephen-built diesel engines appeared to cost more than those of our competitors and I brought this up at several board meetings, but John D'Arcy would accept no criticism of his Engine Works. In 1962 he left to take up a position at Pametrada, the marine industry turbine designers, which suited him as the job was technically orientated. It would be at least six months for a successor to take over so a holding position was required. John Robson could look after the technical side and Norrie McCrae the Outside Engineers, but there was nobody suitable for the Engine Works. The Board ganged up on me saying "You were the one who criticised it, you run it". Thus I found myself running the Engine Works for over six months in addition to my other responsibilities.

As I was not a practising Engineer I lacked experience with machines and had little idea of the right course of action, but I knew that our costs were too high and the management structure seemed over elaborate. I called in the consultant who had helped improve our stock control system and his report confirmed my feelings, but the position was even worse than I thought, as little had been done to improve productivity for over 40 years. Piecework times dating back to 1926 abounded, even though new machines which could do the work in a fraction of the time had replaced the older ones. Machine tools were not cutting anywhere near their capacity although they turned away merrily with the appearance of total efficiency.

Machine selection, particularly in the heavy machine shop, was also shown to be poor with a complete absence of milling machines. The Engine Fitters and Boilershop showed similar inefficiencies. All shops were on piecework with times for each operation to be carried out and evaluated and the operator paid accordingly, but the suggested way forward was Measured Daywork which was an up-to-date and sophisticated variation of piecework giving a more predictable wage. The consultant had set the ball rolling but I had not the knowledge to set the system up so it would have to wait.

The consultant's report also suggested halving the number of managers so I bit the bullet to remove a complete layer of management and had the unpleasant job of sacking four managers. Three, all effective men who thoroughly understood the situation, took it well. I was not sorry to lose the fourth but, when I told him his bad news, I have never seen anyone so shattered. I considered parting with a fifth but, having already halved the number of managers, was concerned about leaving too many gaps. One of the three was re-employed three years later when a vacancy occurred.

Several machine tools which had not been used for years were sold. There were two antique vertical slotting machines or 'wall creepers', one made in 1891 and the other in 1896 which had been essential when we built reciprocating steam engines. I did not have the courage to get rid of both so kept the newer machine as it took up very little useful space but some of the old hands in the machine shop then told me that I had scrapped the wrong one. Several years later we were able to get subcontract work for the remaining machine which was one of the few in the country suitable for cutting long slots in the inside of cylinders and it worked continuously for two years.

When we came to select D'Arcy's successor one candidate seemed to be tailor-made for the job so Oliver Blanford, who was a Management Consultant with wide experience in Measured Daywork, started with the Company at the end of 1963. His remit was to improve productivity and find suitable new products for the Engine Works and if possible for the Shipyard. I was off the hook but pleased to have started in the right direction for Oliver to take over. He knew exactly what he was doing in the shops, set up the systems, put them into operation and productivity increased dramatically as soon as the scheme took effect. This was the start of an eight year period over which productivity in some areas of the Engine Works almost doubled.

The Amalgamated Engineering Union took a more flexible and responsible attitude than the Shipyard Unions and fully accepted the principle that production had to be efficient while the workforce were sensible and loyal. Measured Daywork had recently been adopted by other engineering companies in the area so reaching an agreement to our proposals was not difficult. The boilermakers in the Engine Works were more in tune with AEU thinking than with the diehard shipyard model and accepted the new ideas. Having established the new system throughout the Engine Works, Oliver set about Measured Daywork for the Outside Engineering Department, which fitted out the ship's engine rooms and installed the engines. Theirs was a more complicated operation interacting with shipyard trades and subcontractors and the work was less easily defined. In the Engine Works, existing staff set the targets but, for the ship work, a small team had to be taken on. Nevertheless we were hopeful that the scheme would yield benefits which might lead the way to improve shipyard productivity, and Oliver said he was confident that he could produce results as good as he had done in the Engine Works. The guinea pig was the ship *Zealandic* and the systems were set up but, until she was completed, the savings could not be assessed. At the beginning of 1966, to our considerable surprise, Oliver announced that he had accepted the appointment of Managing Director of Fairfield Glasgow and left two months before

Zealandic's completion. We now waited with bated breath to see what savings the Outside Engineers would make on this ship.

Oliver had set up Measured Daywork very effectively although some people complained that if he saw anything moving, it was immediately put onto Measured Daywork. He had applied his skill to the Engine Works and now we needed somebody who could reap the benefits. We were lucky to have the right man in the wings. Tom Evans was a director of Simons Lobnitz who had started his career in the Simons drawing office to become Chief Draughtsman and had just finished the unenviable task of completing production and closing down the Simons Lobnitz Yard at Renfrew. He had done this most effectively and his drive, bluntness and integrity were exactly what was needed in the Engine Works. One of the first things that Tom did was re-examine the overheads where he made substantial savings, and then set about bringing discipline and order into the organisation.

Our Engine Works was not big enough to survive long term by building diesel engines and while Oliver was in charge the Board had taken a decision to diversify into other products. However we made a mistake by subcontracting the last two Sulzer engines which we had on order as we could have done with the turnover. Productivity was improving dramatically but this meant that more work was needed to fill the shops. From then onwards the main problem was always getting enough turnover to keep the Works in full production.

In the early 1960s the future of shipbuilding looked uncertain and the Board decided that we needed new products for the Shipyard and the Engine Works. Diversification was all the rage at that time and we hoped it might answer some of our problems. When North Sea oil started to be developed, the Shipyard had considered the possibility of building oilrigs. Much time was spent examining triangular jack up platforms designed by Le Tourneau which were uncomfortably wide for our berths. Getting them down the river would not have been easy and there was relatively little fitting out work so the proposal was dropped. Several years later Lithgow's built an oilrig at Port Glasgow and it was a financial disaster, so our decision not to proceed with rigs was almost certainly right. Ship shaped rigs only came into prominence after we had stopped shipbuilding.

Oliver had joined us with skills which no other Director possessed and seemed to be the ideal person to pursue diversification so he was given free range. Many possibilities were investigated and rejected but three were taken on. The first and largest was Pitt Trailers, an English company making trailers for articulated road vehicles, which we bought intending to move production to Linthouse. It did not take long to discover that Pitt's financial and production position was much worse than expected and heavy losses were being incurred. Bringing the work to Linthouse was much less attractive when examined in detail and only one small assembly unit was transferred. Even that was kept separate and operated under Pitt management rather than Stephen's. When Oliver departed, Pitt Trailers was still losing money at a substantial rate.

On land and sea the use of containers was increasing dramatically and this looked a good field for the future. A company making container handling equipment was bought, and with it came Commander Watkins RN. It was renamed Alexander Stephen Cargo Handling Equipment or ASCHE. Their main product, the 'Conjac', was a straddle carrier which, in conjunction with a tractor, lifted and transported containers. It could not stack them and was therefore only suitable for depots with relatively few containers. The Conjac, designed for 20 foot containers, had some success and a design was produced for 30 foot containers, but ASCHE lost money regularly and produced no work for the Engine Works. Watkins was sure that there was a rosy future and the Stephen Board still hoped that the venture would become profitable.

Our third diversification, Hydel, was to design and develop a drilling machine to sink holes for wells and suchlike. It was the brainchild of Robert Penney, a great enthusiast, who had had some success with smaller machines. We designed a machine to drill holes up to 2'6" in diameter which would have been an excellent product for our Engine Works and the conception was good and well thought out. But when Oliver left, Penney had not been able to get a single order for this machine and Hydel, with no income, was also losing money.

Oliver left us when all three diversifications were making substantial losses. They needed a lot of management time and Jim, who had worked with Oliver on diversification and was now the only person in the organisation familiar with these companies, took over the responsibility. In all cases Jim found the situation worse than expected and the hope of achieving profits faded everywhere. By now the shipbuilding industry was under surveillance by the government and it was becoming clear that they thought that mergers were the way forward. Merging could only be investigated by top management so our diversifications could not get the attention they needed, but hindsight shows even a genius would have had difficulty in making any of them successful.

Diversification for Shipyard fitting out trades was continually sought. Ships' crews were being drastically reduced and the new generation of ships carried no passengers, so fewer cabins were required creating spare capacity in the Joiners' Shop. A salesman was taken on to obtain joiner work and one or two interesting contracts were obtained. Church pews provided an alternative line and it was noted that the specification for the Catholic churches was generally higher than that for the Protestants. However, the return obtained from what the salesman could produce hardly covered his salary so the project was eventually discontinued. Odd jobs were taken on by other departments but the inescapable conclusion was that a shipyard was suitable for building ships and for little else.

Attempts at diversification were nothing new. I was once hunting for something in our Office basement and came across a file on a 1927 patent to reduce a ship's resistance through the water by blowing bubbles from its bow. There is no record of this scheme being tried and many years ago the patent had been deemed of no value. Stephen's held it jointly with John Tutin, the designer and inventor who had designed the *Queen Mary's* rudder and had also patented steel hatch covers and stabilizers. For some reason we also held the patent for the Tutin Teapot which never caught on and was certainly not a suitable product for shipyard diversification. John Tutin was the father of Dame Dorothy Tutin the actress who had been one of the heartthrobs of my youth and when I got in touch with her, she was pleased that her father was still remembered saying that she felt he had never received the recognition he deserved.

CHAPTER 8

The Struggle, 1960–64

To suffer the slings and arrows of outrageous fortune
– Hamlet

At the beginning of 1960 Alexander Stephen & Sons was still shaking off the effects of disastrous demarcation strikes and trying to regain the momentum which had been lost. The Repair Department Director Willie Johnstone had joined the firm in 1915 and become a Repair Manager in 1928. He had gone on to run the department successfully until he took ill and died suddenly in August 1961. Jim and I missed his advice as he had been a wise old bird and a father figure to us both. Though Norrie McCrae had been taken out of Repair to run the Shipyard, there was a man of stature in Denny McGuffie, an Engineer who took over and continued to run the Department with great efficiency.

After the war continental shipyards had been laid out and re-equipped for welded ships avoiding the labour pitfalls which existed in Britain. Here the Boilermakers' Union still showed contempt for anything which would improve productivity. A new machine might reduce the number of operatives from four to one but when the Union insisted on two, it was a less attractive proposition. The British Shipbuilding Industry has been criticised frequently for not modernising but Stephen's did modernise and it very nearly bankrupted the Company. Even after we had got over the severe labour troubles, the benefits we had hoped for never materialised. We could have gained efficiency by increasing the labour force but welders remained in short supply. The Boilermakers' Union restricted their numbers and would not accept that semi-skilled operatives could do the simple jobs. We were being beaten on price by continental yards, some of which were heavily subsidised and the Japanese were becoming a serious threat. Their new industry was growing and had already thrown off the "Made in Japan" label which had been synonymous with shoddy goods. For the first time since the war the supply of ships overtook the capacity required with the result that freight rates dropped and the whole shipbuilding market tightened up. Our regular customers were liner companies whose trade had been with the colonies and their business was in decline.

We gained a new customer in 1961 with an order for two 6,900 ton cargo liners from T & J Brocklebank, who had had a 49% shareholding in Hamilton's of Port Glasgow and had previously had their ships built there. When Hamilton's was bought over by Lithgow's, Brocklebank realised they could get better designed ships elsewhere. Their Superintendent Engineer Captain Sydney Jenks was attracted by our technical skill which helped us to get the order. Our Engine technical department under Malcolm MacGregor had been developing engine room models. Computer science in this area was still in its cradle and our modelling technique was well ahead of the game. Brocklebank's typical cargo was light, so volume in the holds was paramount. Our model produced a more compact engine room which saved two frame spaces so an extra 5'6" of the ship became available for cargo. Malcolm also developed the first ship's bridge control for Sulzer engines which was fitted in the second ship *Mahout*[1] under the name of Mahout Engine Bridge Control. It worked perfectly and we sold several installations to other companies. However we had no sales force to market it effectively and it never achieved the success it deserved. The press was invited to *Mahout's* trials and over 20 reporters enjoyed a day's outing. A somewhat

1. Plate 15.

pedestrian *Financial Times* reporter accepted our handout for it to appear almost verbatim in the *FT* but the brightest was from the *Daily Express*, then the top newspaper. He went all over the ship asking searching questions and gave Malcolm a thorough grilling but the *Express* headline next day was "Engineer thinks up invention in his bath".

Enquiries for passenger ships were rare and attracted the fiercest competition but in 1961 we obtained an order from British Transport Company, the marine arm of British Rail, for the Harwich/Rotterdam ferry *Avalon* of 13,500 tons. No provision for motor vehicles was specified by BT, a serious misjudgement as this was a fast expanding market, so the ferry was out of date before she was delivered. The ship was launched by Mrs Beeching, wife of Dr Beeching, Chairman of British Rail, who was about to wield his axe on hundreds of miles of railway. Having had all our orders on a cost plus basis, we were now having to accept fixed prices. Delivery times were shortening and materials were becoming more readily available but inflation was getting out of control. If we under-allowed for it we lost money and if we over-allowed we did not get the order. We had expected a small profit on *Avalon* but it turned into a loss.

We continued to build for our regular customers, Elders & Fyffes, Shaw Savill and the P & O group where *Piako*, a refrigerated and cargo ship of 9,985 tons fitted with a Sulzer engine, was the third ship of that name[2] built by us for New Zealand Shipping Company. The first had been a sailing ship in 1876, the second a steamship in 1920 and the third a diesel refrigerated vessel in 1962. *Antrim*, delivered the same year, was an almost exact repeat of *Donegal* built 5 years earlier. Our regular customers were feeling the draught as our order book continued to shrink and finding work to keep the Yard going became vital.

2. The first and third *Piakos* are shown in plates 16 and 17.

Like most British shipyards we struggled to deliver our ships on time. We had set up an efficient planning office using critical path analysis and other modern techniques, but it did not help when a strike or late delivery of machinery caused unavoidable delay. As a ship neared completion, more people worked on board and therefore much of the labour costs occurred in the last three months. Our Planning Department devoted considerable effort to assessing by analytical means the time required to finish a ship which was expected to be completed in a month, but the best estimates at that stage were still made on the spot by an experienced shipbuilder, though the Planning Department made an invaluable contribution for the earlier stages.

Denny's of Dumbarton went into liquidation in 1962. They were a family firm similar to ourselves and while we competed in some areas, our two families had been friends for four generations. When work stopped at their yard a ship which was being built 'on spec.' still lay half built on the ways. Whenever a prospective buyer showed an interest, the Trade Unions, led by the Boilermakers, made it clear that no work would be done unless all the workers were paid rates which were totally unaffordable, so the whole Denny labour force was paid off except for a few security men. Union Officials declared with gusto that the ship could rot on the berth. However after it had languished for over six months, we got in touch with shipowner Jack Bilmeir and indicated we could finish the vessel for a reasonable price using the materials Denny had already bought, subject to Union agreement. The Unions turned the proposal down flat at first but eventually agreed, with the rather unexpected but logical condition that no ex-Denny man should be employed on the ship. Contracts between ourselves, Bilmeir, the Liquidator Robert Smith and the Unions were then worked out and signed. Our men were bussed daily to Dumbarton to complete the steelwork for the launch, after which the ship was brought up river to Shieldhall

Wharf to be fitted out. All went remarkably well in spite of hitting an unusual snag concerning the launch. We used our own launchways and other equipment although our procedure was almost identical to Denny's except that they did not use drag chains. The river Leven allowed ships a very long launching run so Denny's ships were launched free of encumbrances and then, at the appropriate moment, an anchor was released and the ship's windlass was used to slow and stop the ship. Only a senior Denny's shipwright and his mate, who had been performing this task for years, could do this so the Unions had to be brought in. They showed common sense and made an exception to their ban, so these two men were taken on for the launch and did an excellent job. After the launch a small lunch party was held on Denny's premises but in spite of Jack Bilmeir's sunny personality it seemed more like a funeral. A former Director of Denny's who was one of Bilmeir's guests was overcome with grief and broke down during the speeches.

The Unions continued to show a sensible attitude. Everything went to plan with *Melbrook* being handed over on time.

Bilmeir was an ebullient character and a successful shipowner who had taken considerable risks in his earlier days. By 1963 he was regarded as a highly respectable citizen and known to be a friend of Winston Churchill. He was kind enough to ask Sue and me to his pheasant shoot at Tilmouth Park which he ran as a hotel. We met Max Faulkner among the party, an Open Golf Champion who was the professional at Sunningdale, Jack Bilmeir's Club. Max was less skilled with a shotgun and our host warned us that 'when Maxie fires we all duck' but we also learned that 'when Maxie fires at hares we all jump'. Jack and his wife gave us a memorable weekend. It was a great shock to us all when Jack Bilmeir died suddenly just before the ship was delivered and within days the Denny Director who had found the launch heartbreaking had also died.

Early in 1963 the dredger builders Simons Lobnitz of

Renfrew announced that they were closing down. William Simons and Company had been an old established yard which built ships up to 6,000 tons of which a fair percentage were dredgers. Lobnitz & Company had specialised in bucket dredgers, cutter suction dredgers and rock breakers. Sir Fred Lobnitz, the founder, had married the sister of Weetman Pearson, later Lord Cowdray who was probably the most successful British businessman of his generation, with Mexican Eagle Oil the centre of his empire. Cowdray had huge influence in the ports in Mexico and South America so almost all the dredgers there were built by his brother-in-law. The Company later made an unusual contribution in World War II by helping to design the Mulberry Harbours for D-Day which consisted of a series of platforms linked together. At the corners of each platform were vertical posts or 'spuds' which dug into the sea bed, the platforms rising and sinking with the tide in a way similar to which cutter suction dredgers operated.

The adjoining Simons and Lobnitz yards merged in 1957 but it was not a success. Normally shipbuilders have a friendly rivalry with their neighbours but it was not like that in Renfrew. They hated each other. If an employee was seen speaking to anybody in the rival company, even in a pub, a severe telling off could result and disciplinary action had been known. Their mentalities were different; Simons thought like shipbuilders whereas Lobnitz thinking was dominated by the complexities of dredgers. Both shipyards were entered from Meadowside Road in Renfrew. Simons employees walked along the north side and Lobnitz kept to the south side and the rival factions never talked to each other. So deep was their animosity that, after their companies were merged, the two teams never got on edgewise. Simons built 'dredgers' and Lobnitz 'dredges'. To me a dredger is a ship with dredging machinery and a dredge a bit of machinery wrapped round by steel to make it float. Because I am a shipbuilder rather than an engineer, I have standardised on 'dredger' throughout this book, but accept that even fifty years on, any Lobnitz ex-employee would cut me dead, convinced that I had sided with the opposition.

Two years later G & J Weir bought the merged company. John Spurr was taken on as Managing Director and was a first class marketing man setting up a very effective sales organisation, but production was blighted by conflict between the two warring factions and, although Spurr was a great diplomat, he was not a production man and failed to build an effective organisation. The hope had been that overheads could be halved and production doubled but that showed signs of being reversed. Weir's finally decided to call a halt and close the yard. We were approached with a view to our taking over the Company. Our relations with Weir's were close as we undertook a steady stream of work for them in our Boilershop. The Stephen and Weir families had known each other for generations. My brother Jim and I shared a small grouse moor at Cleughearn in Lanarkshire while Lord Weir and Russell Lang, Chairman and Vice Chairman of Weir's, owned Carrot Moor next door and we merged the two very successfully. Taking on the Shipyard at Renfrew was not a starter for Stephen's but building dredgers at Linthouse was. Consultants assessed the dredging market and concluded that it was not a growth market but would remain relatively stable. We finally agreed with Weir's that they would remain responsible for completing the ships at Renfrew and we would take over the Simons Lobnitz goodwill which consisted of the design team and the sales force as well as patterns and drawings. No money changed hands as the agreement was that Weir's would get half the profit from any orders which might emerge from promising enquiries which included 6 suction dredgers for Russia and a tin dredger for Indonesia. The Unions were surprisingly co-operative perceiving it as the only way any of the business could be saved. *Skitterness,* a trailing suction dredger for the British Transport Docks Board, yet to be laid down, was transferred to Linthouse. At 1,677 gross tons she was a very small ship for us but our facilities coped efficiently and our engineers had no problems with the dredging machinery. She was launched by Mrs Robens, wife of Alf Robens, Chairman of the Coal Board and one of many extremely able men who had come up through the Trade Union movement.

John Spurr's job had evaporated and he soon left Renfrew but he could not have been more helpful, giving us an accurate picture of his team's strengths and weaknesses. SL key technical and sales teams were absorbed into our organisation and were fully occupied on dredger work. Their sales force consisted of Jimmy Hamilton with two assistants, Cyril Hudson in London and a man in India. It was all rather out of our normal line but I became responsible for their sales team and found myself dealing with almost all SL matters at Linthouse. Tom Evans was left in charge at Renfrew to complete the ships there and close the yard down.

The most advanced enquiry was for a tin dredger for the Central Management Board of Indonesia who wanted 70% of the price on credit over 10 years. We had to arrange the credit and insure it with Export Credit Guarantee Department, a very well run Government Department, essential to all exporters, which insured the credit risks presented by foreign customers and their countries. The shipbuilder paid the premium and added it to the price of the ship. Most technical matters concerning the dredger had been agreed but the credit terms for a volatile country like Indonesia took time. When ECGD was finally satisfied, the contract was signed, Jimmy Hamilton having worked tirelessly on it for months. The tin dredger *Banka*[3] consisted of a non-propelled rectangular platform 300' × 80' × 19'6" deep supporting machinery to dig up and process tin ore from the sea bed. Where heavy tin ore had been deposited alluvially, it had sunk down over the millennia to

3. Plates 26 and 27.

PLATE 1. Sir A Murray Stephen 1892–1974. Chairman and Managing Director. (portrait *c*1950)

PLATE 2. John G Stephen 1894–1970. Shipyard Director. (photograph *c*1935)

PLATE 3. Jim Stephen 1923–1993. Chairman and Managing Director. (photograph *c*1960)

PLATE 4. Sandy Stephen born 1927. (photograph 1954) Later Managing Director and Author.

PLATE 5. Linthouse Shipyard and Engine Works 1946. 15 ton berth cranes and the fabrication bay had recently been installed as the beginnings of the modernisation programme. Note the passenger ship, top left, being converted from a troop ship back to her normal use. See also plate 33.

PLATE 6, ABOVE.
The Main Office at Linthouse in 1916. The Author's office was on the ground floor at the nearest corner. The flag is the Stephen Company and family house flag – a light blue Maltese cross on a white ground. Today the building is little changed and still in use, having been renamed 'Alexander Stephen House'.

PLATE 7, RIGHT.
The cruiser *HMS Kenya*, launched by the Duchess of Gloucester in 1939. The ship accelerates down the ways. The drag chains shown in the foreground will shortly bring her to a halt.

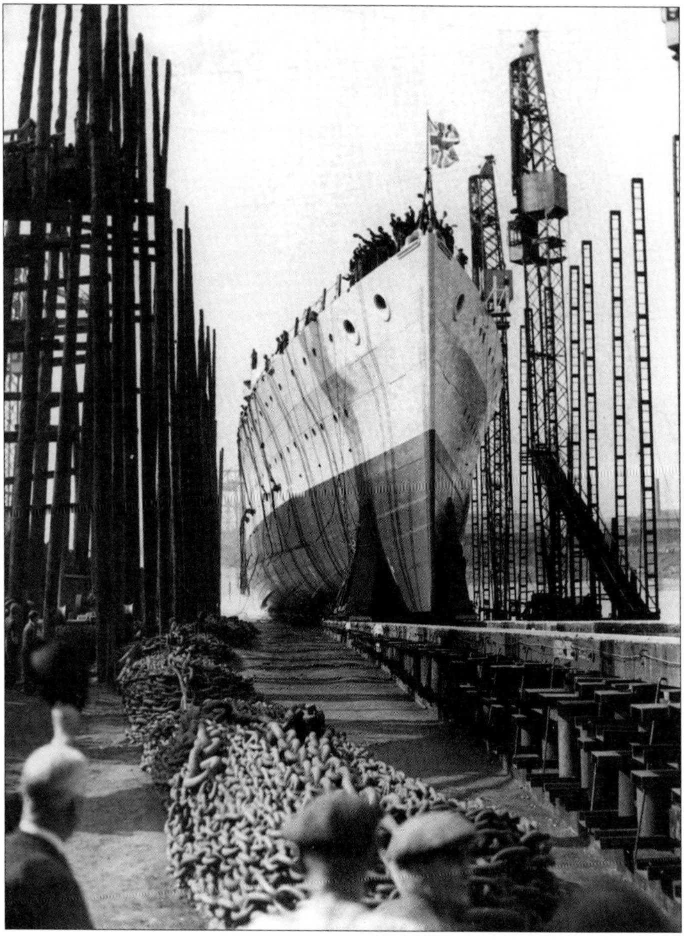

PLATE 8. *Aureol* 1951. Built for Elder Dempster and carrying 329 passengers, possibly the most elegant passenger ship of all time.

PLATE 9. *Camito* 1956. Built for Elders & Fyffe. Passenger and refrigerated cargo ship, carrying 200 passengers.

PLATE 10, ABOVE.
Changuinola 1957.
Refrigerated cargo and passenger ship, the first of four sisterships built for Elders & Fyffes. She carried 24 passengers.

PLATE 11, RIGHT.
Turbines being tested in the Engine Works for installation in *Chicanoa*, sistership of *Changuinola*.

PLATE 12. *City of Melbourne* 1959. Built for Ellerman Lines.

PLATE 13. *British Bombardier* 1962. Built for British Petroleum, this tanker was the largest ship built at Linthouse.

PLATE 14. *HMS Zulu* 1964. Frigate built for the Admiralty (now the Ministry of Defence) undergoing sea trials before commissioning.

PLATE 15. *Mahout* 1963, built for T & J Brocklebank. The Mahout Bridge Control System, designed at Linthouse, was the first remote control system to be fitted to a ship's slow speed diesel engine.

PLATES 16 AND 17. The first (TOP) and the third (ABOVE) of the three *Piakos* which were built at Linthouse for New Zealand Shipping Company – 1876, 1920 and 1962.

PLATE 18, RIGHT.
Majestic 1967 Refrigerated cargo motor vessel. Ready for the launch.

PLATE 19, BELOW.
Launch party with John MacConnachie of Shaw Savill, his daughter Janet and Jim Stephen nearest the camera.

PLATE 20. ABOVE.
Miss Janet MacConnachie pulls the handle, releasing the ship as the bottle breaks on the bow.

PLATE 21. LEFT.
Majestic enters the Clyde.

PLATE 22. *HMS Hermione* 1969, the last warship to be built at Linthouse being moored at Shieldhall wharf after her launch.

PLATE 23. *Terra Nova* 1894 carried Captain Scott to the Antarctic in 1910. Sunk off the coast of Greenland in 1943, her wreck was discovered on the seabed in 2012.

PLATE 24. *Forceful* 1925 for Australian United Steamship Navigation. Coal burning tug still afloat in the Queensland Maritime Museum

PLATE 25. *Ribbok* 1967. Trailing suction dredger for South African Railways, designed to dredge the harbour at Durban.

Banka 1965. Non-propelled tin dredger built for Central Board of Management, Indonesia.

PLATE 26, TOP. At Shieldhall Wharf.

PLATE 27, ABOVE. Being towed to Indonesia by a single tug.

PLATE 28. *Severodvinski* 1966. Trailing suction dredger for Sudoimport of USSR shown after her launch with the Stephen shipyard cranes in the background.

PLATE 29. *Arabatski* 1966, sister ship of *Severodvinski* leaving Shieldhall Wharf for her trials.

PLATE 30. *Nassau Bay* 1965 Cutter suction non-propelled dredger for Construction Plant Facilities, an offshoot of Costain Construction.

PLATE 31. *Port Chalmers* 1968, built for Port Line. Newly launched before the tugs have passed up their hawsers. She has come to a stop pointing up and down the river exactly as planned.

PLATE 32. *Port Caroline* 1968 Sister ship of *Port Chalmers*. The last ship to be built at Linthouse.

become concentrated above the bedrock. The bucket chain of the dredger stripped off the overburden which was deposited astern by means of a long conveyor belt. The ore rich layer was then taken on board and panned in a series of vibrating hoppers to get rid of the lighter impurities, and finally relatively pure tin ore was put into sacks to be taken ashore. A system of winches and anchor wires allowed the vessel to move forwards and sideways to cover the ground. When a major move was required a tug lifted the anchors and towed the dredger to its new position. This dredger was to work off the island of Banka on the east coast of Sumatra, 300 miles south east of Singapore. Tin dredgers usually worked inland, built on site and launched into small ponds specially dug for them and were normally of an all riveted structure, but we built a more efficient welded hull. Welded superstructure would have saved little, so the traditional riveted design was accepted.

Although the structure was unusual for Linthouse, building was straightforward apart from getting the huge bucket arm from the fabricating shed into its position on the berth. It was 230 feet long and weighed 360 tons without its 15 cubic feet buckets which were to be fitted after the vessel got to Indonesia. Discussion took place as to whether the bucket arm should be put together in the fabrication shed and skidded out to the berth in one piece or whether normal sized units should be joined up on the berth. The first option was selected but, as we had never before skidded anything so large, the safety angle was taken very seriously. Our Safety Officer, Malcolm Campbell, rushed around like a blue based baboon to ensure that every possible precaution was taken. The operation went without a hitch, the only casualty being Malcolm himself who fell and damaged his leg[4].

4. I found out about this many years after it happened from George MacMillan, the MacMillan Clan Chief, who had been working in the Shipyard at the time.

When *Banka* was being built, there were riots in Djakarta. Sir Andrew Gilchrist, the British Ambassador and a Scot, was besieged in the British Embassy, but became world famous as his remedy to keep the rioters at bay was to play his bagpipes on the embassy roof. Our tin dredging consultant, a cricket loving Englishman, seemed unduly depressed after the event. We tried to persuade him that all would be well for the contract and he eventually admitted his sorrow "They dug up the cricket pitch in Djakarta". Superintendent Engineer Apitule was resident during the building work. He was Indonesian and very good value, with a Dutch wife who looked most elegant at the launch wearing her sarong along with the other Indonesian ladies.

Smit, the Dutch towing experts, towed *Banka* out to Indonesia with a powerful single tug and the cost of this long and arduous tow together with the insurance premium for the voyage accounted for over 10% of the total value of the contract. Windage was reduced by leaving off the corrugated iron roof and side walls. When the tow was fifteen miles off a lee shore on the south coast of Ireland a gale sprang up and the tug was at one time steaming into the wind on full power but the whole tow was moving backwards at three knots. The tow rope broke but the crew managed to run another wire. How this was achieved remained a Smit trade secret. After that panic, the tow proceeded smoothly and *Banka* was safely delivered and set to work without any major problems.

Another legacy from Renfrew which I had to deal with was Hymatic Dredges, a separate company owned 60% by Hay's Wharf and 40% by Simons Lobnitz. Hymatic supplied small dredging units which could be transported by lorry but unfortunately the company ran into an insurmountable problem, so Hay's Wharf decided it should be put into liquidation. I felt rather bad about this as our ethos was to get things right, but it was a correct decision and nobody lost out seriously.

I had benefitted by using consultants twice but we began

to use them too often. They were of use where we lacked wider knowledge, but on organisation they rarely helped. We commissioned reports which finished up stating the obvious and giving information that was already known. The cost was never added up, but we should have been more selective.

Our order book was still shrinking but the labour force was showing signs of being more co-operative. We hoped our productivity might improve and were negotiating an interchangeability agreement to allow us to increase the steel throughput in the Fabricating Bays, but we were still short of welders. Because we needed work we quoted keen prices, hopeful that our labour costs were going to improve and that inflation would slow down.

Stephen-built ships meantime plied the ocean and most ended up in a scrap breaker's yard many years later, but the sad ending of *Bear*[5], a sealer built at Dundee in 1874, deserves to be mentioned. In 1932 she was used by Admiral Byrd for his expedition to the South Pole, thereafter becoming a much loved training ship for the United States Navy. She had the distinction of being the only ship in the US Navy ever to be built outside the US. In 1963, after she had been retired, she was being towed to become a major feature in a maritime museum but was lost when she foundered in a gale.

5. Plate 46.

CHAPTER 9
Fairfield's

We are the stuff that dreams are made of – The Tempest

In October 1963 Fairfield Shipbuilding and Engineering called in the Receiver. They had gone bust before in the 1930s and had been rescued by Sir James Lithgow, much against the wishes of the rest of the shipbuilding industry. We had been in direct competition for almost every type of ship. Their demise would have removed one competitor and allowed us to take on some of their men to increase our production, but our relationship with them had always been good, so we would have missed a friend and neighbour. I had once spotted a trailer load of launchways going out of the main gate and telephoned our Head Foreman Shipwright to be told that they were going to Fairfield's for their next launch. When I asked how much he was intending to invoice them for the loan I was told "Nothing; we are borrowing their drag chains for our next launch". Top management should keep their noses out of some things.

We were still assessing the effect of the closure when the bombshell came as Sir Iain Stewart announced his intention to rescue Fairfield's with the help of the Labour Government. He ran Govan based Thermotank, which specialised in ventilation and air conditioning systems. Stewart was a visionary on labour relations and while his visions were laudable, his feet were not on the ground as he believed he could take over a shipyard, negotiate a new code for labour and revolutionise labour relations and productivity. He ignored the fact that every shipyard taken over by non-shipbuilders since the War had failed dismally. Jim, who knew him well on the Employers' Federation, was sceptical about the labour relations at Thermotank. Stewart's plan was bound to have a disastrous effect on Clyde shipbuilding and on us in particular. The Shipbuilding Industry needed reduction in capacity and my father sent the following telegram to the Opposition leaders Sir Alec Douglas Hume, Edward Heath and Tom Galbraith "HOPE YOU WILL PROTEST AGAINST GOVERNMENT TAKE OVER IN FAIRFIELD. QUITE UNNECESSARY. OTHER YARDS ALL SHORT OF MEN. JUST POLITICAL STUNT. THIS WILL BE VERY DISTURBING INFLUENCE ON OTHER YARDS & LESSEN THEIR CHANCES OF SURVIVAL. NET LONG TERM EFFECT ON CLYDE WILL BE BAD. HAVE NO CONFIDENCE IN STEWART". He was proved right on every point.

Stewart's ally in the Labour Government was George Brown, President of the Board of Trade and an ex-Chancellor of the Exchequer. Brown thought that this social experiment was a splendid idea and persuaded the Government to finance it. This was made easier by the fact that Fairfield's was the largest company in Govan and the Constituency seat could be lost to the Scottish National Party at the next election if Fairfield went under. Thus, with some contributions from others, Fairfield Glasgow was set up in a blaze of publicity. It was significant that the new company refused to join the Shipbuilding Conference which dealt with the affairs of the Industry and the Clyde Shipbuilders' Association which was concerned with labour matters. Though every other shipyard belonged, Stewart wanted to go it alone. My brother Jim was invited to his house to meet George Brown who put intense pressure on him to become a Director of Fairfield's, but Jim said that he could not agree unless they modified their views and joined the Shipbuilding Conference. Brown then told him "If you do not join the Board, I will personally make sure that your company never gets another warship order". This despicable threat did not deter Jim who stuck to his guns.

A month later Oliver Blanford gave notice to take up the position of Managing Director at Fairfield Glasgow. Jim had mentioned to Iain Stewart that Oliver had done a good job in the Engine Works in the field of Measured Daywork and Stewart must have taken note of this. While at Linthouse, Blanford had not been involved in any way with the Shipyard or Shipyard Trade Unions, and the only experience he had had on ships was being in charge of the Outside Engineers, having just installed Measured Daywork on *Zealandic*. He tried to persuade Myrtle Collins, his secretary, to go with him to Fairfield's, but, although this would have been a considerable promotion for her, she refused. All Fairfield executives were replaced by managers from outside the shipbuilding industry.

Two months after Oliver left Linthouse, *Zealandic* was completed and we were hopeful that Measured Daywork would bring some savings in labour and that it might be a model for the Shipyard. When the figures were put together we were devastated to find there were *no savings whatsoever* and the additional overhead cost of the staff setting the targets had not been covered. The system was tested on subsequent ships but we eventually concluded that, while Measured Daywork might be appropriate for shop work, it was not suitable for men working on ships. At Fairfield's a wage increase was given to all hourly paid employees for acceptance of Measured Daywork, outlawing strikes and agreeing to consider flexibility and retraining. Measured Daywork was then applied to every department in Fairfield's. We had contacts in Fairfield's at all levels and soon learned that schemes identical to *Zealandic's* had been installed with paperwork unchanged. They did not know that the scheme for the Stephen Outside Engineers had attained no savings.

The savings in the Engine Works were taking longer to come through. In estimating for our ships we had mistakenly accepted figures from Oliver Blandford on savings for the Engine Works which were not achieved. Fairfield Glasgow had nobody in their top management with the experience of shipbuilding. To make matters worse at Linthouse we were discovering the disastrous results of the diversifications.

Fairfield's public relations were by far the best part of their organisation and they soon had the press eating out of their hands. Their company produced a string of press releases claiming huge increases in productivity while denigrating the rest of the industry. They made a publicity film "Bowlers and Bunnets" which was a disgraceful bit of propaganda. In it Sean Connery, the actor, claimed that when a shipyard closed the bosses walked off with the money and the men lost their jobs. He should have known that at Fairfield's it had been the other way round. The Lithgow shareholders, headed by Sir James' daughters Margaret and Ann, had spent almost two million pounds modernising the yard and the bankruptcy meant that they lost every penny of their investment, while every employee was transferred to the new company and lost nothing. The film also trumpeted huge savings in labour costs whereas it was subsequently proved that there were none. It gave details of savings made due to work-study on certain items and operations, though most of the examples shown related to items which had been tackled some years earlier at Linthouse. Another point which the film laid on thickly was how Fairfield's was revolutionising the industry by retraining. There is no evidence that any retraining was done. The Unions never gave an inch over their working practices and it was not long before they broke their promise to banish strikes.

Derek Kimber, the very competent Shipyard Director of Fairfield Shipbuilding & Engineering up to the time the company failed, later told me that the steelwork manhours per ton achieved by Fairfield Glasgow were never as good as they had been in his time. This was confirmed by the report on Fairfield's steelwork by the independent British Shipbuilding

Research Association in November 1968. It showed clearly that no savings in manhours had been made unless measured against the dip in production immediately after closure had been threatened, so the claims made in their press releases had been pure fantasy. At Fairfield's Measured Daywork failed to reduce steelwork manhours, about half of which was shop work, so there was no chance of any beneficial effect on work on the ships, as *Zealandic* proved.

Fairfield's took on new orders for at least two year's work at prices substantially below what the most efficient British shipyards could match. Trying to assess the final profit on a ship even three months from completion is always difficult. Thus the true position can be concealed and figures can be massaged, but when a ship is completed, the truth must out. In Fairfield's case it would be well over two years before true figures emerged. Everything pointed to Fairfield building up huge losses but they continued to churn out highly optimistic press releases. At Linthouse we had clear evidence that they were heading for disaster, but broadcasting the truth would have sounded like sour grapes and the Government was on their side.

As predicted by my father, Fairfield Glasgow had a disastrous effect on all Clyde shipyards. The high rates paid at Fairfield's were well above those of other Clyde shipyards and the Unions put enormous pressure on them all to pay the same. The pressure was such that higher rates had to be conceded not just on the Upper Reaches of the Clyde but on the Lower Reaches as well. Worse than that, Union officials thought they were walking on water and became completely intransigent. At Linthouse all our hopes of improvement were knocked sideways.

The Labour Government's intervention was blatant electioneering and showed up the worst side of democracy; there is no doubt that their rescue of Fairfield's hastened the demise of Clyde shipbuilding. I think Iain Stewart genuinely believed that he could do something to help British industry. However it is my firm belief that, at different levels of management at Fairfield's, attitudes varied from vision, hope, over-optimism and ignorance to downright dishonesty.

CHAPTER 10

Selling Home and Abroad

And yet we ventured, for the gain propos'd
– Henry IV Part 2

Traditionally the Managing Director of a shipyard was the salesman. We followed this pattern and my father was our sales force for many years, keeping in regular touch with British shipowners. Our market had been almost entirely with British liner owners with the occasional foreigner who wanted the type of ship we could build efficiently. Jim took over the British owners from my father and visited them regularly in London. Obtaining an order from one of them was a fairly standard process, usually tendering against several similar British shipyards with negotiations relatively short and contract documents straightforward. On being made Commercial Director I took over the making up of the tenders and the responsibility for foreign sales. We had built very few ships for foreign owners since the war and our contacts abroad were limited. We had no foreign agents, but occasionally a ship broker, who operated in the country concerned, helped us. Almost all our efforts were directed towards British shipowners although we made a big effort to secure a passenger liner for the Norwegian American Line only to be beaten on price.

In 1963 Stephen's put in an offer jointly with Cammell Laird for six cargo liners for the National Shipping Line of Uruguay, ships well suited to our facilities. Soon afterwards the Agent appointed for the job indicated that we were favourites for the contract. The Cammell Laird Sales Director, Norman Cave, and I set off for Montevideo with two merchant bankers from Baring Brothers, because credit was required, and also a Spanish speaking London lawyer because the contract would be under Uruguayan law which was basically Napoleonic. The concerns about Uruguayan law were sorted out with surprisingly little trouble and the issue finally centred on the credit which was for 70% of the contract value over 10 years. Export Credit Guarantee Department (ECGD) had to be satisfied that the customer was creditworthy and they laid down stringent conditions. The customers were, as in all South American countries, short of cash but it looked as though the contract might be brought home.

We dealt with one Uruguayan legal company, regarded as an 'honest lawyer', concerning the details of the contract and with Monsieur Supervielle, also honest and greatly respected, for his contacts. He was French Uruguayan and his English was not strong so he had to put up with my appalling French. At one meeting with him our problems seemed insoluble and he said "I will go and see the President. He is a friend of me", but it was to no avail. Several 'less honest lawyers' who approached us were referred to our hard working agent.

As the contractual and financial points polarised the team gradually returned home until I was on my own in Montevideo trying to get the credit arranged. This dragged on and on. Communication with home was difficult with telephoning almost impossible. The most reliable link was Telex which worked most of the time but the messages often got garbled. My taped telex to Norman Cave in Birkenhead usually started "Please get Mr Cave to come to the Telex and answer the following questions ... Meantime here is my progress report ...". By the time the message had printed itself out Norman had got to the telex, read the questions and sometimes the answers could be typed back there and then. On one occasion he sent me the telegram "WELL KNOWN MARINE JOURNAL STATES ON BEST AUTHORITY THAT THE ORDER IS GOING TO THE SPANISH STOP COMMENTS

PLEASE STOP CAVE". My first thought was to refute it in one word but realised that I could get another word in without paying extra so I sent across the Atlantic what must still have been one of the shortest telegrams on record "ABSOLUTE BALLS STEPHEN". When it arrived at the Cammell Laird switchboard, the girls were too shy to take my rude message in to Norman.

The Uruguayans I met were delightful, very hospitable and pro-British. The Battle of the River Plate in 1940 was still their big event and it was not 'the British and the Germans' but 'us and them'. The junior merchant banker and I were invited by the honest lawyers to an estancia for a weekend. It was in beautiful rolling grassland and, although I had been put off horses many years before, I was mounted and greatly enjoyed my ride as the country was open with a fence and gate only every two miles. During dinner of barbecued lamb, our host told us about the carpincho which he said was an animal like a pig but had the head of a hippopotamus and lived among the trees lining the rivers. This appeared to us to be the Uruguayan equivalent of our joke about haggis hunting and we went along with it. We thought they had carried the jest rather far when, after our very good dinner, they packed us and a rifle into a small car and drove across the plain. After ten minutes the headlights showed up exactly what had been described. We were both flabbergasted. I was invited to shoot it but declined and the merchant banker, who had imbibed even more than I had, took the rifle and fortunately missed.

I was pleased to be befriended by British Embassy officials who introduced me to some interesting people. I was invited to a Montevideo Chamber of Commerce lunch and sat next a highly cultured Uruguayan businessman who visited London from time to time and had flown on to Glasgow specially to see Salvador Dali's 'Christ' in the Kelvingrove Art Galleries. To my shame I had to admit I had never seen it, although I have since put that right and consider it a great painting. I was even roped in to help entertain the Corps de Ballet of Sadlers Wells who had just finished touring South America when their plane home from Montevideo was delayed. It sounded a wonderful invitation but the poor wee lassies were dead on their feet having spent the previous night waiting at the airport.

Latterly I had time on my hands in Montevideo so I spent hours trying to learn Spanish with singularly little result. I struggled to study the language in the evenings and made very little progress but did learn that 'River Plate Spanish' differs from what is spoken in Spain. I always took an hour off for a drink and a simple dinner. The bar had a large selection of Scotch whiskies and I had a different one every night but I avoided the last one in the row which was a Uruguayan whisky made by ANCAP, the Ministry of Cement and Petroleum. As my workload decreased I also played a few holes of golf at the Montevideo Golf Club, a pleasant course designed by Bobby Jones.

After I had been there a month, Uruguay had a financial crisis which eventually caused four of their leading ten banks to go bust. Our consortium tried all possible means to help them raise the money but in the end realised that they would be hard pressed to raise the 'payment with order'. Even if they had managed that, ECGD's conditions would have been hard to meet so, after accepting that the order would never be placed, I reluctantly left for home. The only good thing about my two month stay was that the Uruguayan peso had almost halved in value relative to the pound and as I paid my hotel bill on leaving, my sterling traveller's cheques went much further.

Back at Linthouse I had to get to know the Simons Lobnitz sales organisation. Their small London office was a convenient base for any Stephen staff visiting the capital but it was expensive to run and so was Cyril Hudson who was SL's London Sales Manager. He was doing sterling work in Russia at the time and was a great mixer but his expense account was astronomical. He was later awarded the OBE for his work although I reckoned Jimmy Hamilton was equally deserving. SL and Stephen's sales business did not overlap so their sales organisation remained intact. Dredgers had a long life while the parts wore out, so there was a very profitable spares business which had to be run efficiently.

Simons Lobnitz had tendered for six trailing suction dredgers for Sudoimport, USSR who showed considerable interest. It was at the height of the Cold War and many had doubts as to whether it was morally right to trade with the enemy. On the other hand we knew that our competitors had no such scruples and the British 'powers that be' had encouraged SL so we followed up the enquiry hoping to land a profitable contract. Moscow had already been visited several times and at the beginning the Russians put a tail on Cyril Hudson, but the commercial position remained favourable although progress was slow and tedious. As the pressure was too much for one person, we went in pairs and I did a couple of stints to help Jimmy Hamilton who masterminded the operation. Intourist allocated visitors to one of several hotels in Moscow and never put two business colleagues on the same floor. The worst hotel was the Ukraine, a multi storey Christmas cake type monstrosity where I was on the 14th floor and Jimmy was on the 5th. The stairs were forbidden and floor 13 did not officially exist but was known to be for 'technical services', which meant bugging. We had to use the slow and overcrowded lift system to get from one room to the other, changing lifts at floor 7. The quickest time to the other room and back again was 20 minutes. Restaurant service everywhere was appalling and a simple meal took at least two hours. There were however places which served a very reasonable sandwich and tea 'chai limonen', served in a glass with a metal handle.

The Russians had recently subverted British Embassy staff – the Vassall case was forever being quoted – and the Foreign Office was determined that businessmen should keep out of trouble so anybody going to Moscow was thoroughly briefed. We were warned that when we retired to our hotel room on the second night in Moscow, the harridan who sat in the lobby watching our every movement would probably pass a message to the KGB who would take action 15 minutes later. Sure enough exactly 15 minutes after I entered my room the telephone rang and a sexy female voice said "Allo daaarleeeng". I put down the telephone as instructed. We knew our hotel rooms were bugged, and if discussing contract details, we made sure what we said would not help Sudoimport by writing down key figures and words. Turning the bath taps full on was another effective but unpeaceful way of achieving privacy. Safer still was a walk outside, but in November this meant walking on a cold snow covered pavement. Nowadays even that would not be safe.

Our only competitor was IHC of Holland, the world's largest dredger builders. We knew them through the Dredger Builder's Association whose members were ourselves, IHC, Ferguson Brothers of Port Glasgow, Orenstein & Koppel, better known for their escalators, as well as a shipbuilder from France. Each company registered their dredger enquiries with a well-trusted London lawyer called Hutton, whose parents I had known in my youth. He would analyse the enquiries and all interested builders would be informed of the competition. When the Association met in Brussels, which was about twice a year, the official meeting was formal with little divulged. After that, informal meetings took place to discuss enquiries we had received. Some of the deals done would probably be illegal now but they were sensible and I don't think any customer suffered. The friendly Managing Director of Orenstein & Koppel was an ex-U-Boat Captain Karl-Friederich Merten. I lost contact with him when I stopped being a shipbuilder but later read about a reunion of his U-boat crew with the crew of a British ship which he had torpedoed in the Indian Ocean.

IHC was summonsed to Moscow at the same time as

ourselves and also came in pairs, Sudoimport putting us through the mangle on alternate days. We were confronted by a team of five who spoke only Russian and an interpreter who was a granny. Every possible obstacle was put in our way. One day they announced that they were going to pay for the ship in oil, and demanded an appropriate quotation. A trading company called Golodetz had a man in Moscow who told us that the Russians had no oil to export so this was just a ploy, but we had to produce a quotation at the next meeting. Another tactic was to keep us at the meeting from morning to evening without food or drink. They would go out of the room in turns and come back wiping crumbs off their mouths, so to counter this we always took iron rations in our briefcases. Once Jimmy Hamilton made a provocative remark and, when the granny interpreted it, the head Russian exploded and a long stream of Russian invective ensued. Granny blushed to the roots of her grey hair and when he at last stopped she interpreted "Mr Volkov says that he does not agree with you". Some things were predictable. When told "Your price is too high. It is higher than the Dutch" we answered "If you wish to buy cheap ships, buy from the Dutch. Our ships will be working long after the Dutch ones are on the scrap heap". We knew that this would be levelled at the Dutch next day and spent that day trying to work out exactly what their defence would be. In this case we concluded that they would say that we added unnecessary metal and that our design was poor. Sure enough at our next meeting we were told "Your ships are too heavy. The design is not good".

A few days after arriving in Moscow I got flu and had to take to my bed. Trying to order food on the telephone was hopeless so Jimmy asked the girl in hotel reception if they could send up a bowl of soup for me that evening. The answer was "Niet". "So my friend must starve?". "Yes". He knew the form and having waited until she had gone off duty he arranged it with a more accommodating lady. He did this for three days and always asked for it for 7.30 p.m. My frugal meal arrived, once at 7 o'clock, once at 10.30 and once somewhere in between. Sudoimport were surprisingly sympathetic and sent a doctor to visit me. He gave me a thorough inspection and prescribed mustard plasters which were sheer agony so I decided that that being ill was too dangerous and made a hasty recovery.

Sometimes we left meetings in despair and wondered if it was worth continuing, but the Commercial Councillor at the British Embassy, Dougal Stewart, was our refuge in times of trouble and the solid rock who kept us going. After one really difficult session we told Dougal how the Russians had dismissed us in scathing fashion. Dougal's reply was "If they said that, you are really getting somewhere". We were being entertained by him and his wife in their flat one evening, discussing the negotiations as usual, when he suddenly made an inane remark. I looked at him in surprise and he just pointed to the ceiling as he knew that his home was bugged. Dougal was 'the Stewart of Appin' holding the secret of the Appin murder in 1715, but this was the only point on which he would not help us. Sir Dugald, as he became, went on to be an Ambassador.

The discussions with Sudoimport became more focussed and the Russians dropped a hint that the order might be split. After more visits to Moscow a contract for three ships was signed. It had taken 6 man months in Moscow to get that order. Two weeks of being bugged in Moscow had a strange psychological effect on me and for two weeks after I got home I had an irrational feeling that I was being bugged in my own home.

I paid several visits to Latin America where Lobnitz dredgers generated good spares business. Our Agent in Mexico City was a very nice ex-RAF Wing Commander Duncan who had been shot up badly during the war and had emigrated for the sake of his health. While there I was invited to buy a Shipyard at Vera Cruz on the East coast by Senõr Pagliai one of

Mexico's millionaires who was Italian by birth and married to Merle Oberon, the film star. It was a typical Latin American project where somebody had started to build a shipyard, run out of money and left it to rot. It would never have been a proposition for us but I made a gesture by offering to supply technical help if somebody else took it on. Not surprisingly it came to nothing.

My last visit was after the Wing Commander had sadly died and his business was being continued by his wife Pamela. The enquiry I was following up was for three trailing suction dredgers for the Mexican Government. Our price was just over £1,000,000 per dredger but the contract price was £4,000,000, the fourth million to be paid surreptitiously to finance the RPI, the political party which had been in power for many years. The ships would, of course, be built on credit and very surprisingly Export Credit Guarantee Department accepted the extra million because they appreciated that without sweeteners there would be no order[1]. It was suggested that I should draw £1,000,000 in dollars from the bank and go to the Ministry with my suitcase in one hand and the contract to be signed in the other. I would almost certainly have been mugged on the way, but could not refuse at that stage as it was part of a negotiating process. Venal characters who were fixers, known as 'ferrets', were in evidence. One suggested to me that if we got the Admirals on our side the order would be in our pocket. He wanted to arrange a party for them with girls – £100 for a top quality girl for the Admiral in charge with other girls at £60 and £40 for those of lesser rank. I declined. The contract had to be signed before the President retired a year later, but the project ran out of time.

Argentina had a regular need for dredger spares and our

1. Nowadays our Government frowns on 'commissions' or bribes. It should be made clear to them that in some countries no orders will ensue without bribes. We cannot change the way these countries are run.

agents in Buenos Aires were of British descent, both partners having fought for Britain in the war. I also chased an order for a new dredger but without success. I had issued an edict that our staff should travel tourist class on long journeys by air and take a day off to recover. Having set the example I made this clear to our agent but, when he met me at the airport, he said that the government official who I had to meet was going on holiday the next day, so I just had time for a quick shower when my jet lag had hardly had time to set in.

I arrived at Buenos Aires but my luggage didn't as British Caledonian Airways had many problems on this route. After three days I was becoming unacceptable so decided to buy some underwear, shirts and socks. The shops suggested were 'Harrods' and 'James Smart of Edinburgh' so, being a patriotic Scot, chose the latter. I went to the appropriate counter but the girls did not understand English and my Spanish was limited to ordering an omelette and beer. Eventually I was asked to wait – 'Minuto' – and a young man appeared and said in faultless BBC English "May I help you, Sir". He was a British Argentinian who had served in the Royal Marines. My luggage arrived the next day.

Our agents also represented the predecessor of British Aerospace for whom they were trying to sell an executive jet to the President of Argentina. I went with the agent out to the airport and met the legendary test pilot Captain Cunningham. The President had been taken up on a flight and wanted to visit his village out in the pampas so Cunningham had agreed to land him on a field, having first been assured that the pampas, being alluvial, had no stones. The President thought he would easily recognise his village but Spanish designed villages were identical and all looked the same from the air. Eventually Cunningham flew to the Andes, took a fix on a mountain and navigated back to the correct village. I did not fly in the jet but was aboard when it taxied from one side of the airport to the other.

I investigated another possible order for a dredger in Columbia, visiting Bogota first and then the port of Baranquilla where the river Maddelena required dredging. Some years previously a lighthouse had disappeared when millions of tons of silt slid into a vast chasm on the ocean floor. At one spot the depth of the water had been 6 metres in the morning but 40 in the afternoon. The Maddelena thereafter had continued to deposit silt and the channel was silting up again. A dredger was not needed full time and in the end they did the sensible thing and hired a dredging contractor. Our agent in Columbia was Senõr MacGregor who was very proud of his Scottish descent. His great-grandfather had emigrated from Scotland but the name was now pronounced *Ma* gre *gore*.

One of our first jobs abroad was to call on the Commercial Counsellor at the British Embassy, usually the least effective person there, so we got singularly little help. The shining exception was Dugald Stewart in Moscow who was everything we could have asked for. Most of our ambassadors considered trade to be beneath their dignity and in all my visits I never once met a British Ambassador. We were at a huge disadvantage compared with the Dutch whose ambassadors acted as additional salesmen. The staff at the Uruguayan Embassy were outstanding for making my long stay in Montevideo tolerable but they couldn't help us get the contract.

The excellent network of Simons Lobnitz agents helped in far flung countries and I met many very interesting people. My work was occasionally exciting but it was mostly drudgery – long flights, delayed flights, jet lag and much hanging around between long hours of intensive work. Hotels were generally confortable but had little local colour and bedrooms made bad offices. When my foreign forays ceased in 1968 and I was glad to pay more attention to my much neglected family.

CHAPTER 11

The Years of Pain, 1965–66

When sorrows come, they come not single spies, but in battalions – Hamlet

Jim had been appointed Deputy Chairman in 1961 and gradually took over his father's executive functions becoming Chairman in 1964. Sir Murray remained on the Board in an honorary capacity and did not attend meetings. He had had an illustrious career with a First in Engineering at Cambridge and would have got a Rugby Blue but for a serious knee injury. He was a contemporary of Rupert Brooke at King's College and his rooms were on the same staircase as the economist J Maynard Keynes who never once spoke to him and probably regarded him as a thuggish rugger playing Scot. My father's troublesome knee did not stop him playing hockey for Scotland and climbing the Matterhorn long before fixed ropes were introduced. He joined the Royal Artillery at the start of World War I and was awarded the MC. On the Somme in 1918 he was captured when his gun battery was supporting Portuguese infantry who 'vamoosed' leaving him surrounded by the Germans. After several escape attempts he ended up in a prisoner-of-war camp on a small island in the Baltic which was the World War I equivalent of Colditz. He rarely talked about this unhappy time and he never forgave the Portuguese. He treated the finer points of engineering with disdain. During World War II he was driving home in the blackout when the engine of his car appeared to explode. Having stopped and looked under the bonnet, he could see nothing wrong. Surprisingly the engine restarted, although vibrating badly, and he trundled home. Next morning he noted a large hole in the side of the engine where one of the pistons had gone through the side of the crankcase but the engine started yet again so he hiccoughed the 16 miles to Linthouse, left a message for the mechanic, George Burney, and started his work. Twenty minutes later a furious George, who had been trained to perfection by Rolls Royce, burst into his office and told his Chairman that he was 'not fit to be in charge of a motor car'.

My father had represented the shipbuilding industry as Chairman of the Shipbuilding Conference and served as President of the Institute of Marine Engineers and of the Institution of Engineers and Shipbuilders in Scotland. He was knighted in 1946 and was universally respected throughout the Industry. In those days when an important person died, the BBC broadcast a five minute eulogy before the Nine o'clock News. But when asked to do this for a prominent British industrialist who had recently died he declined, as Stephen's had suffered more than once through the dealings of the deceased. Two days later the same BBC executive telephoned and said "I have approached other people who have all refused, but every one insisted that you are the best man to do it". He gave the eulogy as he had done on several other occasions.

Outside shipbuilding he had many interests and honours including directorships of London, Midland and Scottish Railways (LMS), Scottish Western Investment Trust, now Murray International Trust and other companies; he was a member of the University Grants Commission, Honorary Treasurer of the Scottish Conservatives and an Honorary Doctor of Glasgow University but he probably valued his appointment as Lord Lieutenant of Lanarkshire above all the others. In spite of these public achievements he was happiest in his old clothes, going around his land clearing a drain, cutting up a fallen tree or stalking a rabbit with a dog and a gun.

My brother Jim could not have taken charge as Chairman and Managing Director at a more difficult time. When Oliver

Blanford left to go to Fairfield's he was not replaced and his responsibilities were spread. The Engine Works was taken over by Tom Evans reporting to Jim. The Engine Technical Department, where Malcolm MacGregor had the design side well under control, reported to John Robson, our Naval Architect. The Outside Engineers Department came under shipyard control where Norrie McCrae's shiprepairing experience was invaluable while Jim took on responsibility for diversification in addition to his already heavy load.

On the dredging front *Skitterness* and *Banka* were followed by the three Russian trailing suction dredgers *Severodvinski, Onegski* and *Arabatski*[1]. This promised to be a profitable contract but there were unexpected complications. Sudoimport, our customer, had three Resident Inspectors, one of whom was certainly a KGB officer keeping his eye on the other two. They were highly suspicious of anything we did and created problems wherever they went. We had to co-operate with MI5 and the Ministry of Defence because the frigate *HMS Phoebe* was being built on an adjacent berth. The Ministry was surprisingly relaxed about the Russians and only stipulated that the Inspectors were not allowed on board the frigate and, more importantly, were not allowed anywhere near the Admiralty Drawing Office (it was still called that even though it was officially the 'MOD Drawing Office'). The wife of the Russian Ambassador to Britain launched *Severodvinski* and my wife Sue sat next to the Ambassador at lunch. Our daughter Alexandra was just a year old when he explained that 'Sacha' was the Russian shortening of both Alexander and Alexandra, so from then on she enjoyed being Sacha.

The worst mishap of my shipbuilding career happened while *Severodvinski* was being fitted out at Shieldhall Wharf. The hull valve for the dredging tube, which was almost a metre in diameter, had been fitted before the launch, with the internal

1. Plates 28 and 29.

tubing and pump to be fitted later. Before the tubes were in place, power was connected to the valve. Somebody accidentally pressed the wrong button and the valve opened. Water flooded in, but a total disaster was avoided by one of our engineers shutting the valve before the ship sank, although the pump space was flooded and all the machinery got a taste of Clyde water. It was soon pumped out and most damage was put to rights relatively quickly, but the electric motor driving the pump had been under water and might have to be rewound. It went back to Associated Electrical Industries who dried it out, gave it a thorough testing and to our great relief pronounced it to be satisfactory, but the operation took three months.

The Russian specification had extremely stringent requirements on noise level in the accommodation so, at the official tests, we ensured satisfactory readings in the cabins by leaving the doors open and standing our people in positions where they mopped up the sound. The ships were to have been delivered at three monthly intervals with the installation team moving from one to the next. The three month delay to *Severodvinski* forced us to put *Onegski* back as well which played havoc with our production and the expected savings of repeat ships were not obtained. The rest of the building went reasonably well in spite of the Russian Superintendents, but a sparking problem on the electric generator was not completely cured until *Severodvinski* had been in operation for three months. After delivery we got no information on how or where the ships were working although an occasional order for spare parts was received, but *Severodvinski* returned twice to be overhauled by our Repair Company. We had been insured for the flooding accident but the consequential costs were enormous and there was also a late delivery penalty. The disruption and lateness and the fact that Simons Lobnitz had underestimated the complexity turned a profit into a loss. The agreement with G & J Weir was that our profit from contracts would be shared but losses had not been envisaged. We had to bear the total loss on the Russian dredgers, but what we lost was balanced by half of the profit on the *Banka*.

The dredgers were followed by the Royal Naval Fleet Auxiliaries, Logistic Support Ships *Sir Galahad* and *Sir Geraint*. These were ocean-going tank landing ships with a full vehicle deck and accommodation for several hundred soldiers. The order was obtained against fierce competition and improved productivity was essential if we were to avoid a loss so their fitting out programme was carefully planned. They were good ships for us with adequate fitting out work. Twin medium speed Mirrlees diesel engines were specified; our slow speed engines would not have fitted under the vehicle deck. Main engines were normally lowered into place after the launch but in this case they were to be installed on the berth so that the steel units for the vehicle deck immediately above, and the decks above that, could be erected to allow fitting out to start. Delivery of these engines was therefore critical and we had a safety margin of six weeks. Right from the start we pressed Mirrlees and their parent company Associated Electrical Industries, one of Britain's largest companies, to be on time, but the engines for the first ship were not delivered to suit our building plan. I went to remonstrate with Sir Arnold Hall, their Chairman, but the delay was attributed to their subcontractors who were fabricating the 'A frames' for the engines. Our carefully prepared plan had gone haywire so we instituted plan B, fitted the decks above the engines and cut smaller holes for the engines to be lowered through. They still did not arrive so we had to change to plan C. The holes in the decks were filled in again to allow fitting out to get started, then hull plates, auxiliary machinery, piping etc. on one side of the engine room were removed so that the engines could be skidded in sideways. The engines were eventually delivered almost nine months late.

The extra cost of removing and replacing the hull plates and the auxiliary machinery was small compared with that of the disruption to the programme. The second ship's engines were delivered three months later so we were at least able to change to plan C earlier. The vessels had been planned to be completed six months apart and this could not be reduced so the second ship had to go back by the same amount. They were completed without any further disasters but, to add to our woes, it also became clear that our estimate on fitting out hours had been on the low side in the first place and, high tensile steel, specified in some areas, had cost us more to fabricate than we had expected. Man-hour targets were badly adrift and unwanted wage increases in a time of very high inflation caused a heavy loss on the ships.

The ships were shallow draft with Flume passive stabilisers which consisted of a tank on either side of the ship with a large connecting pipe. Water flowing from side to side was controlled to reduce the ship's rolling. They were not as efficient as fin stabilisers and the ships were still liable to roll. There was enough rough weather during the trials in the Firth of Clyde to make life distinctly uncomfortable but it must have been much worse in the open sea. I was in charge of *Sir Geraint's* trials and after they had been completed the Ministry of Defence officials indicated they were not satisfied with the pop riveting in some engine ventilation trunking which measured 24" × 18". We hadn't helped our cause by leaving a temporary stiffening cruciform inside one trunk and this had come adrift during the trials and they were afraid that further debris would get into the fans. I surprised the Ministry officials by putting on overalls, getting a torch and crawling inside the trunk. I considered the standard to be adequate and as they clearly had not been inside I won the point.

Ships' trials were a great change from normal routine. A group which included shipowners, shipyard directors, managers, technicians and tradesmen, all with their appropriate equipment, embarked at Greenock early in the morning to be taken to the ship anchored off the Tail of the Bank. Trials usually lasted two days with the first spent swinging the compass, testing main machinery controls and all other machinery and equipment to ensure that everything in the ship was fully operational. Throughout, there was frantic activity to ensure that the ship met the satisfaction of the crew. Caterers were employed but sometimes the ships' crew undertook the work for training purposes. The second day was usually taken up by speed trials on the measured mile off the Cock of Arran when the top brass gathered on the bridge wing with their stop watches to ensure that the specified speed was reached. It was a friendly occasion with a certain amount of ribbing about the Naval Architect moving to a different position on the bridge to clock a shorter time. Our trials were always amicable but when Brown's built a ship for the Swedish America Line it was reported that shipowners and shipbuilders were not on speaking terms and stood on opposite sides of the bridge. At the end of the second day the ship would normally be handed over. We never had serious problems on trials but during the First World War a destroyer, not built by us, was undergoing speed trials on the Skelmorlie Measured Mile when her steering gear jammed and she headed for the shore at full speed. Aghast at the approaching danger the lodge keeper of St Fillans House, who manned an entrance by the shore, bravely took defensive action by rushing out to shut the gates. I only went on trials occasionally and had little responsibility until I became Managing Director when things changed. Sometimes an endurance trial continued through the night, but warship trials were measured in weeks rather than days.

HMS Phoebe, which was on the longer timescale of all warships, had been taken on at a cut price to keep our labour force numbers up and we expected to make a loss of £250,000 at the very worst. The ship had to absorb labour from the other ships whose production was held up and then was left short when the need for labour was reversed. The result meant that *Phoebe* was also late in a period of rampant inflation and her loss escalated to over £500,000. This disastrous period coincided with the highest wage inflation of the century which peaked in 1966 with wage rates increasing 18%. All six ships under construction were fixed price contracts and were delivered horribly late. Everything went against us at once. The shipbuilding labour shortage was accentuated by the Fairfield's situation and allowed the Unions to force wage increases far above the rate of inflation which was already higher than expected. During this period our overheads were higher than they should have been and our diversification programme caused a continual drain. We made a loss of £139,998 for the year ending March 1964 then a profit of £183,738 the following year but this was followed by a horrific loss of £1,092,278, with a further £357,055 loss the year after. A firm decision was taken in 1966 that no further contracts would be taken on at cut prices. With hindsight we could and should have avoided some of the pitfalls but the late delivery of the engines, the effect of Fairfield Glasgow and rampant inflation could not have been avoided.

Life was not devoid of lighter moments and an amusing incident was later related to me by David Morris the Ship Manager who was in charge of fitting out *HMS Phoebe*, berthed next *Severodvinski* at Shieldhall Wharf. It was often the custom for a Wardroom to purloin a souvenir as an act of one-upmanship and display it on guest nights as a talking point. The resident RN Officers decided that a 'Hammer and Sickle' funnel badge from a real Russian ship could not be bettered. A delegation approached David but he had already guessed what they were after and agreed to this escapade as others did as well and by a stroke of luck the badges were being removed and put in deck stores while the funnel was painted. All this was passed on to the raiders with a promise that David would see them walk the plank if they got caught. So it came about during overtime on a wet Thursday night two of *Phoebe's* junior officers, dressed as shipyard workers, boarded *Severodvinski* carrying an empty sack. Deftly they collected their booty and faded into the darkness. David watched from a nearby location in case they were called to account by a zealous watchman but all went well. Eventually the brass Hammer & Sickle was proudly mounted in the ward-room with the tally-plate "Captured from the Russian vessel Severodvinski at the battle of Shieldhall". On arrival at Portsmouth *Phoebe's* trophy was the envy of every other ships' company.

Although David Morris was Welsh he eventually retired to Alness in Rossshire. I was in touch with him until he died in his nineties. Long after he had given up work he still maintained that he had no use for 'this retirement lark'.

Peripheral activities at Linthouse managed to survive. The Stephen Recreation Club at Coila Park opposite our back gate on Govan Road had been active since 1920. Employees had contributed a penny a week towards its upkeep, unless they chose to opt out, and the Company covered the shortfall. Tennis, bowls and football were the principal sports and a new hall, built in 1958, added badminton and weight lifting, where we produced several Scottish champions. There was a thriving golf section which ran outings and knock-out tournaments, and some of the keen golfers opted to work on night shift so they could play on a less crowded course on weekdays. I was usually in the Directors' bowling team for the match against the Club and more than once played football against the Boys' Club as part of a somewhat geriatric team which was saved from total humiliation by Alan Blacklaws who had kept goal for St. Mirren. Alan, the Assistant Personnel Manager, had overhauled our apprenticeship scheme to give the best training of any shipyard on the Clyde so it attracted considerable talent. The only negative aspect of our top class scheme was that we tended to produce high-fliers rather than the tradesmen we needed. Our past apprentices included Gus, now Lord,

Macdonald, Dick Douglas for many years a Labour MP, Alec Mosson, Lord Provost of Glasgow and Billy Connolly. The thriving Stephen Boys' Club was just beyond the east end of our property and our apprentices regularly showed their ability in concerts in the Recreation Club Hall. Alan Blacklaws eventually left to join Scottish & Newcastle Breweries and finished up as a Director.

Subsidising the Recreation Club was becoming too expensive so, rather than raise the subscription, a bar was opened which altered the whole aspect of the Club. Committee membership, which had been a labour of love, now became a perk. Some of our more dissolute employees were voted into office by their chums and the bar profits disappeared. We were particularly grateful to Jackson Robertson, our loyal Planning Manager, who took over and ran it steadily and sensibly in his spare time. Jackson, whose elder brother was the Caulkers' Shop Steward, was also our unofficial Poet Laureate writing the most splendid doggerel verses for the Linthouse News, our works magazine. Occasionally there were drunken brawls at the Recreation Club. After a bad one, we asked the Govan Police if the licence should be continued and were told "Keep it going. At least we know where to find the bad hats".

The Ambulance Section dealt with accidents in the Yard and also attended Rangers' football matches dressed in their smart uniform. I often oversaw their annual inspection and was usually 'volunteered' to be a casualty to be wrapped in bandages and toted round on a stretcher.

The Staff Association organised outings and the Annual Dinner Dance to which directors and their wives were invited. Sue and I went most years and I usually had to make a speech. The staff knew who we were and I knew all the staff but it was much more difficult for Sue and neither of us could remember who we had met before. The staff members who attended were usually expert ballroom dancers and while we could cope with waltzes, my usual shuffle was inadequate for tangos, sambas and rumbas. Though we knew the procedure for an eightsome reel, the staff entered into it like a tribal war dance. It was good fun because they were all so friendly and the warmth of their welcome made the evening a happy one, but we were worn out when it was time to go home.

CHAPTER 12

A Sea of Troubles, 1966–67

... or to take arms against a sea of troubles – Hamlet

By the end of 1965 Jim recognised that the job of Chairman and Managing Director, combined with the problems of diversification, was getting beyond him and he called in consultants to report on our executive structure. The one suggestion they made was that I should become Managing Director. This came as a shock to me but because there were other competent people in the company, the recommendation encouraged me to believe it had not been made just because I was a Stephen. The task was daunting but at least I knew the business and could start to relieve Jim immediately of some of the load which was bringing him close to breaking point. Firstly I had to ensure that what I would have to relinquish would be properly managed. Jimmy Hamilton's responsibility was increased to include the day to day administration for all sales. Also, and with some regret I shed buying, estimating, stores, stock control and transport which left me free to tackle the major task of producing ships. My brother continued to look after British shipowners and diversification, so still bore a heavy load because the shipbuilding industry was approaching a crisis.

The disaster of *Sir Galahad* and *Sir Geraint's* engines being late was looming at the time of my appointment and the flooding of the Russian dredger occurred very soon after, so at least I was able to take the direct responsibility off Jim's shoulders. The after effects of the flooding occupied much of my time and there were occasions when the attitude of the three Russian

PLATE 33. Shipyard and Engine Works, 1968

1. Main Office
2. Computer Office
3. A.S. & S. Office after 1968
4. Linthouse Buildings
5. Engine Company Gate
6. Electricians
7. Outside Engineers' Store
8. Canteen
9. Shipyard Gate
10. Old Stable / Plumbers' Store
11. Rivet Store
12. Riggers
13. Light Machine Shop
14. Engine Shop Stores
15. Main Boiler
16. Engine Company Office
17. Shiprepair Company Store
18. Shipyard Office
19. Deck Engineers
20. Main Store
21. Three Crane Gantries
22. To Recreation Club
23. Back Gate
24. Road Transport Garage
25. Steel Pickling Tank
26. Joiners' Sample Shed
27. Carpenters / French Polishers
28. Admiralty Office
29. Joiners / Mould Loft
30. Sawmill
31. Paint Store
32. Sewage Boat Berth
33. Shieldhall Stores
34. Heavy Crane and Office
35. To West Berth and Travelling Crane
36. To Boys' Club
37. Pattern Store
38. Pattern Shop
39. Tunnel Ventilation Building
40. Test House
41. Temporary Building

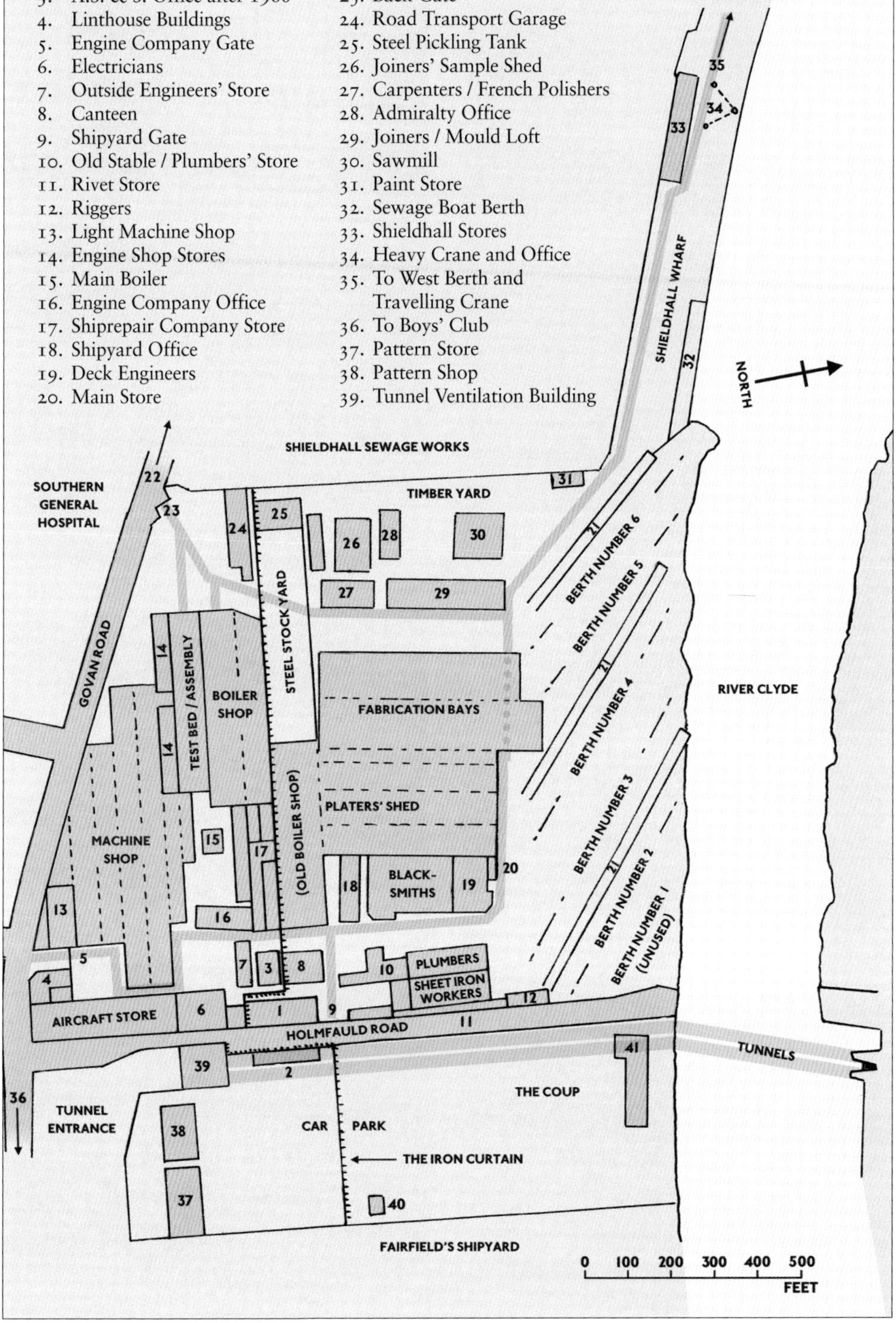

PLATE 34. William Stephen 1759–1838 Burghead – Aberdeen.

PLATE 35. Old Alexander Stephen 1795–1875 Aberdeen – Arbroath – Dundee – Kelvinhaugh.

PLATE 36. Young Alexander Stephen 1832–1899 Dundee – Kelvinhaugh – Linthouse.

PLATE 37. Old John Stephen 1835–1916 Dundee – Kelvinhaugh – Linthouse.

PLATE 38. Fred Stephen 1863–1932 was a Naval Architect designing his own yachts. He was a yachtsman of international repute and Vice-Admiral of the Mudhook Yacht Club of which the Author was later Admiral.

PLATE 39. Sandy Stephen, the author and his wife Sue (2001).

PLATE 40, RIGHT. The Stephen coat-of-arms, now with the Author, was originally registered by Young Alexander about 1870. His mother was a Murray and the three mullets on a chevron represent her family. The right hand represents craftsmanship. The Baron's cap and cape with five gold buttons indicate that the Author is the Baron of Ballindalloch. 'Vi et Arte' can be translated as 'by strength and craftmanship'.

Two pictures of *Dartmouth* 1859 built at Dundee for J. & F. Somes.

PLATE 41, TOP. An accurate representation by an artist who probably worked from the rigging plan. As there is a junk in the background he may have been Chinese.

PLATE 42, ABOVE. An artist's impression which shows a shorter hull with greater freeboard and fewer courses of unusually baggy sails which would not have served well when sailing to windward.

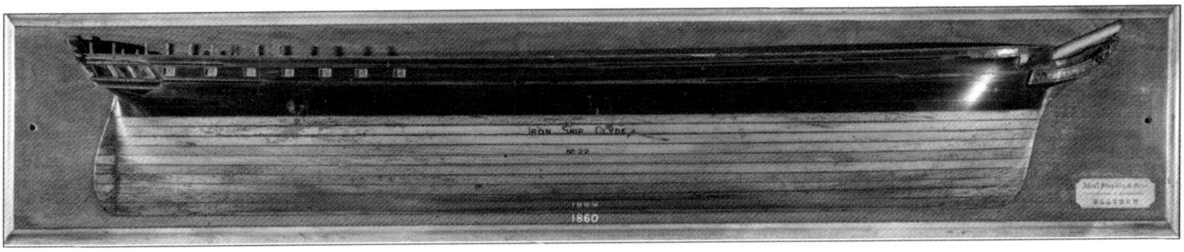

Clyde 1860. Built at Kelvinhaugh for the same owners as *Dartmouth* which was built at Dundee.

PLATE 43, TOP. The oil painting by William Clark shows the ship hove-to while preparing to sail from the Tail-of-the-Bank. Rosneath peninsula can be seen on the left but the town of Helensburgh is hidden by the ship's hull.

PLATE 44, ABOVE. The half block model of the ship was shaped by Young Alexander Stephen. These were made of yellow pine which is a superb wood for carving. In the Ship Drawing Office, a century later, the author used a half block model to work out steel shell plate widths.

PLATE 45. *Shenandoah* 1863, became a Confederate raider during the American Civil War. The oil painting by George Napier attracted much attention when sold by the liquidator of Upper Clyde Shipbuilders at the Sotheby's Auction in 1972.

PLATE 46. *USS Bear* 1874. Built in Dundee, she was the only USS Navy ship to be constructed outside the USA.

PLATE 47. Linthouse Mansion and policies about 1825.

PLATE 48. The River Clyde at Linthouse. In this watercolour the outline of the hills above Dumbarton are faintly visible on the right. The scene was depicted before 1800 when the river was straightened and dredged to transform Glasgow into a major port.

PLATE 49, RIGHT.
The invitation to celebrate the launch of *Glendarroch* in 1870. She was the first ship to be built at Linthouse.

PLATE 50, BELOW.
The spar plan of *Glendarroch*.

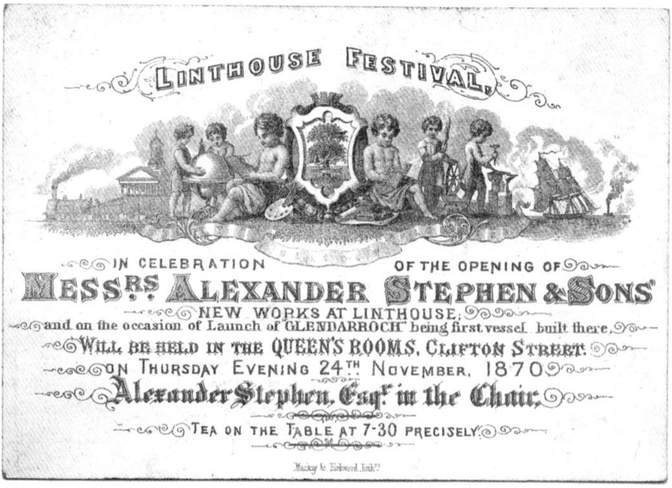

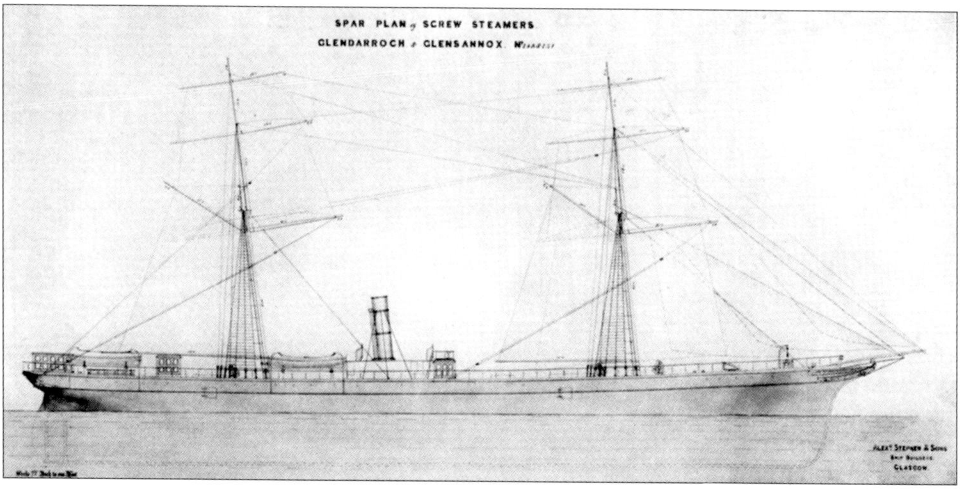

PLATE 51, RIGHT. The Dundee shipyard built the 'snow' *William* in 1846 but this Punch Bowl may have been rejected because it was incorrectly inscribed "Succefs to the Williams. Capt D Young 1846". Though a punch bowl was often presented to a ship by the builder these articles rarely survived life at sea. This one was picked up in a junk shop in Dundee in 1958.

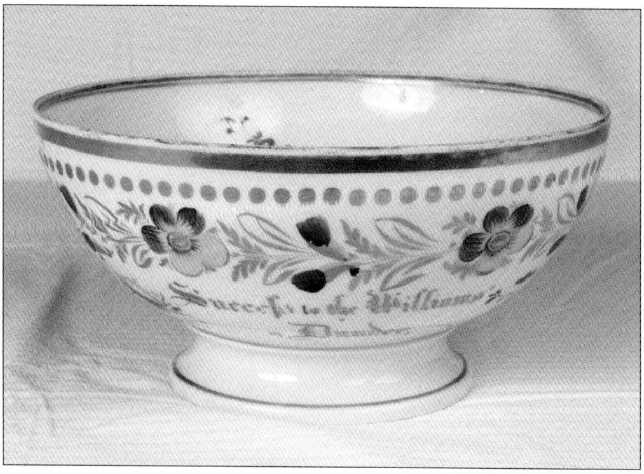

PLATE 52. Field Marshal Prince Barclay de Tolly who commanded the Russian Army when Napoleon invaded Russia in 1812. Barclay was related to the Stephen family.

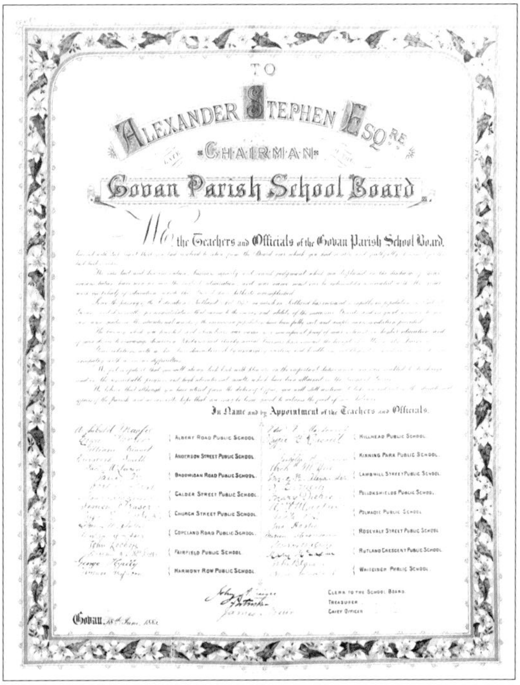

TO
ALEXANDER STEPHEN ESQ.RE
CHAIRMAN
Govan Parish School Board

We the Teachers and Officials of the Govan Parish School Board

In Name and by Appointment of the Teachers and Officials.

Albert Road Public School
Anderston Street Public School
Broomloan Road Public School
Calder Street Public School
Church Street Public School
Copeland Road Public School
Fairfield Public School
Harmony Row Public School
Hillhead Public School
Kinning Park Public School
Lambhill Street Public School
Pollokshields Public School
Polmadie Public School
Rosevale Street Public School
Rutland Crescent Public School
Whiteinch Public School

Clerk to the School Board
Treasurer
Chief Officer

Govan

PLATE 53. When Young Alexander Stephen retired from being Chairman of the Govan Parish School Board he was given this illuminated address by the 16 schools in his jurisdiction. At the time Govan Parish extended from Polmadie on the south side of the Clyde to Hillhead on the north. Young Alexander was also presented with the silver cigar box (PLATE 54, BELOW).

PLATE 55. *Duntrune* 1875. Built at Dundee for the Dundee Clipper Line. Her sister ship *Maulesden* holds the record for sailing from Greenock to Queensland, Australia in 70 days.

PLATE 56. *Cyphrenes* 1872, one of the largest ships built at Dundee was owned by Alexander Stephen & Sons. On her maiden voyage Samuel Stephen, the master, was washed overboard and drowned.

PLATE 57. The *John Lidgett* 1862 showing two other Stephen ships in the background.

PLATE 58. *Viceroy of India* 1929 the flagship of the P & O fleet for many years and the model which was eventually retrieved from disaster.

PLATE 59.

PLATE 60.

PLATES 60 AND 61, ABOVE AND 62, RIGHT.

The steam yacht *Medea* built 1904 now restored at the San Diego Maritime Museum. She was designed and built in 49 working days which would not be possible today. The model made by the Company's modelmaker, used to be in the Author's toy cupboard and was later repaired. Here it displays a more modern funnel added by Fred Stephen, but the Museum has reverted to the original design.

PLATE 63. *Albyn* 1934. One of several Stephen yachts built in the 1930s which survive to the present day.

PLATE 64. *HMS Amethyst* 1943, arriving in Hong Kong harbour after her heroic adventure on the River Yangtse.

PLATE 65, ABOVE.
Olympia 1953. Built for Goulandris Bros., the largest passenger ship constructed by Stephen's.

PLATE 66, RIGHT.
The Georgian sewing table presented to Lady Ramsay for launching *HMS Dunkirk* in 1945. A gift of furniture was unusual as most sponsors chose jewellery when consulted about the memento they would prefer.

Princess of Vancouver 1955. Car/rail ferry for Canadian Pacific Steamship Company.

PLATE 67, TOP. Shown just after her launch when she was the only ship launched at Linthouse with a funnel already in place.

PLATE 68, ABOVE. An oil painting by Bernard Gribble.

PLATE 69. *RFA Sir Gallahad* meeting her sad end in Bluff Cove during the Falkland War.

PLATE 70. The Linthouse Engine Shop after being transported to the Scottish Maritime Museum in Irvine. The columns and roof trusses of the Linthouse Heavy Machine Shop were re-erected to form the centre of the museum.

Inspectors did not help the situation but I was particularly glad to have Norrie McCrae in charge of the shipyard and a supportive team in all other departments. Gradually, all too gradually, the rot was stopped but making up the lost time proved impossible. I was able to address the more basic problems. Overheads were cut – they should probably have been cut deeper but I was afraid that morale might suffer. Departments were judged on the man-hour targets once more and gradually we got onto an even keel. However our programme was six months late and with ships at fixed prices and inflation out of control we were still losing money all the way.

While they provided a sizeable market, dredgers were always going to be a sideline and we needed merchant ships to keep the Yard filled. Shaw Savill, a very old customer, helped us with three handsome refrigerated cargo liners, *Zealandic* then *Majestic* and *Britannic* and they were good people to build for. Unfortunately the latter two ships were being built just after our disasters and their delivery had to go back as well. I went to London twice to tell their Chairman, John MacConnachie, that his ship was going to be delivered late. He was very understanding the first time and said it did not matter too much 'provided we were late early enough'. The second time, he politely said he wanted his ship and not excuses, which was unanswerable. The two points he made have stuck in my mind for the rest of my life. He was a really likeable man, and it was an added pleasure that his daughter Janet was the sponsor at *Majestic's* launch which is shown in plates 18–21.

John MacConnachie was the only shipowner who invited us to suggest names for his ships. Clan Line, Glen Line and Shire Line and suchlike had plenty of choice, but Shaw Savill ships' names ended 'ic' and the best ones were already in use. We were unable to help after *Idiotic* and *Manic* were declared unacceptable. An east coast trawler company ran ships named after rivers with 'ella' on the end. *Tynella* and *Teesella* were fine but they stopped before they got to *Humberella*. The Gem Line, owned by the Robertson family in Glasgow, called their ships after precious stones. Jim Robertson was once asked by a lady from Pollokshields what he did for a living. He modestly replied that he was in the Gem Line. "Ah" she replied knowingly "Robertson's jems and jellies."

We built our biggest trailing suction dredger, *Ribbok*[1] for South African Railways. She was unusual in having an additional dredging tube in her bow for clearing the corners of Durban harbour. I was in charge at the trials and learned that the owners were anxious to test her sand dredging capabilities. Kilchattan Bay was the only sandy bay nearby but I had been forewarned that the sand was too fine to settle in the hoppers. They insisted that we try, so we had a go. The pumps worked away until the hoppers were overflowing, but as we had predicted, little sand settled. We had made our point and they had made theirs. The sand she expected to dig up at Durban would be deposited on the beach where the inhabitants of Durban sported themselves in the summer. Every winter the beach eroded and much of it finished up back in the harbour.

The orders for *Ribbok*, *Majestic* and *Britannic* had been taken on fixed prices and, because they were late, what would have been profits turned into losses. *Majestic* was fitted with a traditional bow and *Britannic* with a bulbous or ram bow. The bulbous bow was the first which we had fitted and it had been developed in conjunction with the National Physical Laboratory at East Kilbride. In service the bulbous bow gave a 5% fuel saving in the ballast condition and somewhat less when fully laden.

For warships a special department was set up to ensure adequate quality as standards were diverging from those of merchant ships. Royal Navy ships gave a good steady base load for labour and we only had to compete against British

1. Plate 25.

yards, so we were pleased to continue in that market. We were delighted to land the order for *HMS Hermione*[2] at a profitable price and just as pleased with orders for two large refrigerated cargo liners for Port Line also at a price on which we could make money. Our good friend Sydney Jenks had moved within the Cunard Group from Brocklebank to join Port Line as Superintendent Engineer and he must have helped channel the orders in our direction.

The efficiency of our fitting out trades left a lot to be desired but there was no quick fix. Each Head Foreman was made more aware that his future depended on the efficiency of his department and was given achievable targets. This helped, but by the time it got seriously under way, we were running short of work and the British Government was putting pressure on all shipyards to merge. Over optimism in the Engine Works started showing up. Savings were still coming but at a slower rate. The effect was comparatively small but Jim was finding that the diversifications were going from bad to worse. Our bank did not help. We had been with the British Linen Bank since the Company came to Glasgow and little changed when the Bank of Scotland took it over. Our relations had always been good but, when we started making losses, they took a hard line and we were faced with the possibility of a Floating Charge. Their attitude seemed unreasonably tough and took up a lot of time which might have been used more profitably.

One positive happening was that the Repair Department bought Harland & Wolff's fitting out basin at Govan in 1965. Harland's had closed their Govan shipyard a year or two before and the rest of the ground had been sold for housing. Their wet basin, between their yard and Govan Drydocks, had lain unused so we paid a modest price. It had to be dredged

2. Shown at her launch in plate 22, she was the second *HMS Hermione* which we had built, the first being a light cruiser completed in 1941.

before we could berth larger vessels and there was little plant other than a geriatric fifteen ton crane. On the other hand we could now repair ships on our own property without any harbour dues being paid. The 'back' store and workshop near the drydock were transferred to the wet basin but the management remained at Linthouse, a mile away.

Until I became Managing Director my only industry commitment was the committee of the Warship Group, a coordinating body under the Shipbuilding Conference who provided an ex-RN officer to back up the Group. Captain John Grindle occupied this position loyally throughout my time and he was a great ally. Jim continued to represent Stephen's at the Shipbuilding Conference but my position changed on the labour side when I became Managing Director. I got involved with the Clyde Shipbuilders' Association, a down to earth organisation dealing with local labour matters. Negotiating with the Unions, the Boilermakers in particular, was a frustrating and tedious business but it had to be done. National discussions were centred on Newcastle and the meetings there were less frequent. On the early morning train from Glasgow, management and Union officials sat in different carriages, each ignoring the presence of the other. At the meetings the battle lines were drawn and the in-fighting was often brutal. However on the train back to Glasgow it was completely different. The bar was packed with both sides intermingling and discussing the day's events. Some problems, insoluble only hours before, found a route to agreement. I was not a star at these negotiations but I avoided putting my foot in it. The discussions were almost all about money and sadly, attempts to improve productivity never even got onto the agenda.

It became clear that our traditional market for refrigerated ships would eventually be taken over by refrigerated containers so we had to get into a new market to survive. Major British shipping companies got together to form two container consortia called Associated Container Transport and Associated Containers Limited. We quoted for three large container ships for both ACT and ACL. The order for ACT went to a subsidised German shipyard whose price was 15% below ours but Stephen's price which included a small profit was second best, ahead of all other British shipyards and Japan. The order for ACL would also have gone abroad but the Labour Government stepped in with a subsidy and the contract went to Swan Hunter. If they had subsidised the ACT order instead, that order could have come to us, and our position would have been enormously strengthened. Luck was not on our side.

From the early 1960s it was clear that British shipbuilding was uncompetitive. Most shipyards in Europe were subsidised and we clamoured regularly for similar treatment. The Conservative Governments were sympathetic to our cause but it was not their policy to hand out subsidies to industry. When the Labour Party got back into power in 1963 we had hoped to gain but they put their money into Fairfield's. The Government resisted a general subsidy and only Swan Hunter benefitted with the ACL container ship orders. Jim was involved in the talks between the shipbuilding industry and the Government of the day and kept the rest of the board in the picture.

When Stephen's order book had lengthened, the delivery times had been too long to turn enquiries for dredgers into orders, and when we could offer a good delivery the orders unfortunately failed to materialise. We were unlucky with two enquiries for large trailing suction dredgers. They did not come to fruition because the Continental owners were unable to raise adequate finance. Our efforts to get new orders were not succeeding.

When Port Line ships *Port Caroline* and *Port Chalmers*[3] were well under way we were asked if the second ship could be converted into a container ship. This would have required a complete redesign of the cargo area and as we had almost

3. Plates 31 and 32.

started construction, there would have been at least a three month delay. As there was no ship to bring forward to fill the gap, it was out of the question.

Production at Linthouse was male dominated but three departments were all female. The French Polishers who worked on furniture made by the joiners produced beautiful work while the Ships' Cleaning Department, was the most efficient department at Linthouse. Mary Skinner ran a squad of Govan housewives, most part time, whose numbers swelled when a ship was being finished. They were a fine bunch of hard workers with no Unions.

In the all female Tracing Office the girls transformed the scruffiest 'pencil on paper' drawing onto 'coloured ink on linen' and their finished products were works of art, made to last. The Office was ruled with a rod of iron by Miss Campbell, a formidable lady, who allowed no male to set their lustful eyes on her girls. When there was a problem with a drawing, the draughtsman would be summoned to a small cubby hole beside the office and Miss Campbell would emerge alone to discuss it. When I was working in the Ship Drawing Office I was invited into the Tracing Office proper to discuss my drawing with a beautiful young tracer. None of my mates in the Drawing Office had ever entered the holy of holies and they maintained that I only got in because I was a Stephen. We were all terrified of Miss Campbell but I got to know her better after she had retired and found her a delightful warm old lady.

Marion Scatchard was a one-off in the Shipyard who had left Cambridge University with an engineering degree in 1952, determined to be a shipbuilder. She applied to my father who told her that women stood little chance of a successful career in the Industry, but she persisted and was eventually taken on. Marion started in the Drawing Office where she was the only woman, but fitted in well, although her ambition was to get onto the production side so, with some reluctance on the part of management, she was appointed as a Junior Fitting Out

Manager. Determined to be more macho than the males, she wore a pork pie hat and trousers, but overdid it when she insisted on being lifted onto a ship's deck standing on the hook of a crane rather than use the gangway like everybody else. One day when walking along the deck she surprised a man having a pee over the side of the ship. "Put that horrible thing away, you disgusting man" became much quoted in the Yard.

It was in her favour that she did not distract the men too seriously as nobody could have called her a beauty, but the Fitting Out Manager found her particularly difficult to fit in and soon she was drafted back to the office to assist Naval Architect David Watson and became an expert on computer design. She later continued her career as a civil servant. Sadly, and possibly because of thwarted ambition, she became reclusive and died in her early sixties. Her life might have been happier if she had heeded Sir Murray's warning about being a shipbuilder, but if she had been born 30 years later she might have had a successful career in the Industry.

Particular mention must be made of David Watson. For many years he designed our ships highly effectively and did all that was asked of him without getting into the limelight. Later he would transfer to Upper Clyde Shipbuilders, but soon left them to run the civil side of Yarrow Admiralty Research Department, the consultants who had up to then concentrated on warships. He ran it very successfully until he retired, after which he wrote *Practical Ship Design* which is now a textbook for every aspiring Naval Architect. In 2000 he was given a well-deserved Honorary Doctorate by Glasgow University to become the second famous Doctor Watson. I am personally in his debt because without his help it would not have been possible to obtain the details of Stephen-built ships completed after 1950 which appear at the end of this book. A keen yachtsman and a good friend, he died in 2007 and I miss him greatly.

While only a shipbuilder with minimal practical experience of naval architecture and marine engineering, I became a

Fellow of the Royal Institution of Naval Architects and of the Institute of Marine Engineers largely by default as anybody who reached a certain position in the Industry was entitled to join. I tried to remain neutral in the ever present but friendly rivalry between shipbuilders and engineers. Engineers were proud of being able to work to a 'thou', a thousandth of an inch, but shipbuilders maintained they got everything exactly right. A perceptive Naval Architect described his trade as "The art of modelling materials we do not fully understand into shapes we cannot precisely analyse to withstand forces we cannot properly assess in such a way that the public at large has no reason to suspect the extent of our ignorance". We Naval Architects are a humble lot, unlike some Land Architects, but claim to be the senior branch dating back to Chapter Six of Genesis, the only doubt being whether Noah was the first Naval Architect or merely a shipbuilder following the omnipotent design and calculations specified by God.

CHAPTER 13
Merging

Uneasy lies the head that wears the crown – Henry IV part 2

The early 1960s saw a number of Clyde shipyards close – Harland & Wolff rationalised by closing their Govan Yard and also closed A & J Inglis which was at the mouth of the Kelvin. William Denny closed in 1963 and Blythswood in 1964. Fairfield's had been rescued by the Government while others were struggling. On 24th March 1966 the long awaited Geddes Report on the state of British Shipbuilding was revealed. Having been commissioned by the Government it reviewed the situation and made recommendations for the future. Every shipyard in the country had been visited at least once and a workmanlike report resulted. In essence it was simple. The industry must forget its old ways, take a fresh view of marketing and companies must merge. The Report nowhere indicated how we could 'forget our old ways' and contained nothing constructive as to how the Management/Union problem could be solved. What was clear was that we could expect no help if we did not merge.

Everybody on the Clyde started talks with everybody else. Big yards talked to small yards, we talked to other Upper Reaches yards and Upper Reaches talked to Lower Reaches. Swan Hunter owning Barclay Curle Shipyard, Engine Works and Ship Repair joined the discussions. The Lower Reaches were concerned that they might have to pay the higher hourly rates of the Upper Reaches and all were concerned that the Trade Unions would jump on the bandwagon and demand higher wage rates. The closure of Barclay Curle's shipyard did little to simplify the situation but positions polarised and serious discussions started taking place between Scott's and Lithgow's, and between Connell's, Stephen's and Yarrow's (CSY). John Brown's would be a difficult bedfellow until the *Queen Elizabeth 2* was finished and nobody wanted to link with Fairfield's.

There was relatively little overlap in CSY. Yarrow's would have built all the warships, we would continue with passenger ships, refrigerated liners and dredgers and Connell's likewise with liners, tramp ships and bulk carriers. The three Chairmen arranged committees to tackle production, labour, accounting, marketing and the technical side. CSY made public its intention to merge as everybody knew about it anyway. Nobody was enthusiastic about merging but it appeared to be the only way forward. We had a special insight as to how the different cultures of William Simons and Lobnitz and Co. could wreck a merger as even at Linthouse their ex-employees still could not get on. The Lobnitz faction had polarised under the technical and sales side and Simons faction within the Engine Works. Cultural differences in other yards were not expected to be as great but could not be ignored. Sadly in April 1966 we had to inform Connell's and Yarrow's that we were expecting large losses which upset the apple cart as the rationale of the merger was that all three companies were more or less profitable. CSY was abandoned although it would have stood a far better chance of survival than the subsequent Upper Clyde Shipbuilders and could have rationalised without costing the Government the millions which it poured into UCS.

The Shipbuilding Industry Board, set up by the Government to oversee all mergers, commissioned consultants to report on the market. They produced a series of curves showing fluctuating demand for tankers, bulk carriers, container ships etc. We had to take notice although they appeared rather fanciful at the time and did not relate to our traditional market. Later analysis showed that their projections bore no likeness to what actually happened.

Meanwhile our board was reinforced when Robert Kemp, a Chartered Accountant with considerable success as a Company Doctor, joined us as a Non-Executive Director. He had impressed us when we dealt with Simons Lobnitz and his advice on merging and on other financial matters would be invaluable; it was a good appointment. About this time Norrie McCrae retired but continued for a spell as a Non-Executive Director. John Pledger took over and ran the Shipyard capably. He was not made a Director because he would have had to spend his time dealing with possible mergers when his whole attention was required to run the Shipyard efficiently.

At the end of 1966 the consultants recommended the merger of five yards – Brown's, Fairfield's, Yarrow's, Connell's and ourselves which became known as Upper Clyde Shipbuilders (UCS) almost immediately. The problems were enormous. Brown's with about 6,000 employees was old fashioned and had no planning department as at Linthouse. They were large compared with the rest of us and their efforts were still concentrated on building the *Queen Elizabeth* 2 whose profitability was uncertain. Fairfield's, with over 4,000 employees, had broken away from the employers' organisations and were busy upping the wages of their labour force and increasing their overheads. We knew that they had taken a course which would bring disaster. Yarrow's was primarily a warship builder, well in with the Ministry of Defence, and could expect to keep a profitable order book. Connell's employed less than 1,000, were efficient with low overheads but might lose this advantage if they became part of a large organisation. We were spread over the range and in a poor position politically, not helped by our short order book. Fairfield's had the backing of the Labour Government and John Brown's wielded a lot of clout. We realised that if any yard closed down it was likely to be us in spite of being more efficient than Brown's and

Fairfield's. If we did not get more orders soon, we would run out of work and have to close down anyway. If we joined UCS, the yard would be closed but at least the labour force might keep their jobs.

Negotiations progressed slowly and time dragged on. The Shipbuilding Industry Board oversaw the proceedings and one of their members, Tony Hepper, took the chair. Each company appointed a merchant banker, whose fees were paid by the Government, to put forward their financial case. We had not used merchant banks in the past, but appointed Lazards. For a long period the bankers fenced with each other but gradually matters resolved and a proposal was tabled which shook us to the core. Stephen's was to remain a separate company with UCS having 25% of the equity but with 75% of the voting rights. It would have been disastrous and, looking back at it now, it was a stupid one to put forward. Our shipyard would have been closed with all the costs from other yards piled onto us, and the Engine Works, Shiprepair and diversifications would not have been able to take any decisions while the UCS Board concentrated on much larger problems. Jim and Robert Kemp, our negotiating team, greatly surprised everybody by turning the terms down flat and telling the Bankers truthfully that we considered liquidating Alexander Stephen & Sons to be preferable. The Bankers got into a huddle and eventually suggested that only the Linthouse shipyard should be taken into UCS. This would leave us with the Engine Works, Shiprepair and our diversifications. It was a poor prospect but at least we would have control of our own destiny.

Fairfield's got some compensation for their shareholders which they did not deserve and we did not oppose this seriously, even though we knew their true position, because getting the merger agreed had become our top priority. Brown's were required to put in extra money and at the last minute we had to add an extra £100,000 (£1,500,000 today). This was almost the last straw but we had to agree. Jim and Robert steered a sensible course to obtain the best deal that could be achieved. As the meetings progressed we got a foretaste of how UCS would be run and were not enthusiastic. Although the Government was putting up money, there was little chance of anything ever coming to our shareholders and we realised that our investment in UCS should be written off at the first possible opportunity. The final papers were signed on 10th January 1968.

We had already split our main activities into Alexander Stephen Shipbuilders, Alexander Stephen Engineering and Alexander Stephen Shiprepairers which required little change but made separation of the Shipyard easier. Jim and I realised that we were working ourselves out of a job, as our Engine and Repair organisations were already competently managed and neither of us wished to join UCS, although Jim became a non-executive Director to protect our interests.

Tony Hepper, who had been much involved in the merger as a member of the Shipbuilding Industry Board, agreed to be Chairman of UCS and appointed non-shipbuilders to run Sales, Production and Personnel leaving John Starks, Brown's Technical Director, as the only person with knowledge of shipbuilding. History had already shown that shipyards run by non-shipbuilders have never succeeded. The most recent case had been where Sir Charles Clore, who had a huge and highly profitable enterprise selling shoes, took over Furness Shipbuilding Company at Middlesbrough. Clore thought that shipbuilders were inadequate and put in his own management expecting to produce a highly profitable yard, but lost money faster than anybody else and Furness soon closed. As soon as UCS was in operation the Unions campaigned to see what they could get out of it. It all looked like a recipe for disaster but we believed the Government would prop them up and that they would always be in a much stronger position than ourselves.

Fairfield Rowan and Yarrow's engine works became the

marine engineering arms of UCS. John Brown Engineering had already been separated from the Yard and had branched out successfully into gas turbines and Barclay Curle Engine Works remained part of Swan Hunter. UCS had no shiprepairing interests and, although there was talk of merging Stephen and Barclay Curle as shiprepairers, the matter never got far.

I was appointed General Manager Linthouse by UCS, although I was not their employee, to keep ship production going until their organisation could take over. Our last ship *Port Caroline* was launched under the UCS flag and Tony Hepper presided. For Jim and me and many others it was not a happy event but we put a brave face on it. At the end of January there was a devastating gale which caused severe damage to property in Glasgow and the deaths of thirty people. At three in the morning I received a telephone call from the Shipyard Gatehouse to say that *Port Chalmers* had broken her moorings at Shieldhall Wharf. I learned that several managers, who were better able than I to deal with such an emergency, were already in action. I then telephoned the police to be told that all roads out of Houston, the village where I lived, were blocked by fallen trees and that any attempt to travel could endanger life. There was only one course of action left so I went back to bed, comforted that the responsibility lay with UCS and not with Stephen's. The ship was soon rescued and tied up again without any damage. When I eventually reached the office the next morning, I was greeted by the news that the wife of a guarantee engineer who was working abroad had just telephoned to say that the roof of her house had blown away. I sent somebody to investigate what seemed to be a tall story, but the roof had vanished and was later discovered two gardens away. The shipyard joiners did a temporary repair which served to protect the stricken occupants until the damage could be fully rectified.

I divested myself of my UCS responsibilities as soon as possible. I was never told when my shipyard appointment ended, so I just let it ride until it became completely honorary though the title never gave me pride. My great sadness in the separation of our shipyard lay in losing touch with so many fine people.

The longer time taken to complete a warship meant that *HMS Hermione* was eventually left as the only ship being fitted out at Linthouse so she was transferred to Yarrow's. She and the slightly older *Phoebe* were to serve the Royal Navy for many years. *Phoebe*, and to a lesser extent *Hermione*, achieved public attention when they featured in the television series "Warship". In service they travelled the world, standing by in crises and patrolling where international incidents threatened. Their careers are now recorded in Wikipedia but most of the fine ships we built plied the oceans doing their job successfully, without receiving the recognition they deserved.

CHAPTER 14

Upper Clyde Shipbuilders, 1968–71

Know we have divided in three parts our kingdom
– King Lear

After the UCS merger was signed the Stephen's Board considered the bleak future. We had

- A substantial but valueless shareholding in UCS.
- An Engine Works in process of diversifying but yet to prove viable and likely to lose its workload for the Shipyard.
- A Shiprepairing company soon to lose its shop facilities and its pool of labour.
- Diversifications all losing money hand over fist.
- An overdraft approaching £100,000.
- Many unknowns to settle with UCS.
- No chance of any government help.

It could hardly have been less favourable. Serious consideration was given to closing everything down, but we decided continuing was a better option. On the plus side, Repair employing about 250, and Engineering with 450, were under the competent management of Denny McGuffie and Tom Evans. They each got on with their jobs while Jim dealt with our diversifications and I concentrated on getting our affairs separated from UCS. Neither Jim nor I ever regretted our decisions not to join UCS and we were immensely thankful that every Shipyard employee was absorbed into UCS, many to continue in shipbuilding until they retired.

The Main Office had been allocated to UCS so Jim and I left our pleasant offices to join the Engine and Repair staff in the dingy but practical office premises on Engine Works territory. Several shipyard activities were based on Engine Works property so the Aircraft Store and the buildings occupied by the electrical, computer and transport departments were rented to UCS. Engineering also had work to complete for the ships building at Linthouse. Conversely UCS provided shop steelwork and other services for Repair and we paid for our share of computer work. All separation took time but the service to us from the UCS computer deteriorated rapidly as bureaucracy took over, so we installed our own smaller computer as soon as we could.

Although the security squad at Linthouse had been officially split, they operated as a team until the Engine Works and Shipyard were physically separated. The boundary agreed between the two, shown in plate 33, was a straight line from east to west with deviations for the Main Office and the computer building. Electric cables together with heating, water and compressed air pipes crossed the boundary in many places, but the services were separated efficiently and in a remarkably short time. Felix O'Neil, the maintenance plumber and a 'weel kent' figure, dealt with plumbing services. Although a UCS employee, his loyalties were with us and it was not long before he transferred to Engineering to complete fifty years service with Stephen's. A new heating boiler for Engine Works and Office made considerable savings. The Shipyard air compressor supplied the Engine Works but UCS were apt to turn it off when it suited them, so we installed our own compressor. For some unknown reason the maintenance electricians had all been allocated to UCS and the squad worked for both companies for eighteen months with the costs appropriately allocated. They were only split when the 'Iron Curtain', an eight foot high wire netting fence was erected between Shipyard and Engine Works, but by then shipyard production at Linthouse had been largely phased out. The electrical substation which was on Shipyard ground continued to supply the Engine Company and we paid for what we used.

Tom Evans worked out a business plan for Engineering which produced a substantial cut in overheads. We retained only two draughtsmen, John Middlemiss and Bob Milligan who had lost an arm when a mechanic in the Fleet Air Arm. In spite of Bob's disability he was highly effective and was later awarded an MBE for his work for disabled ex-servicemen. Shiprepairing companies had never taken on apprentices due to the irregular hours which often had to be worked, and the training of Engine Works' apprentices was becoming increasingly expensive and regretfully had to be phased out. Thus for the first time in over 200 years Alexander Stephen's were to be without apprentices. A strong bond had previously existed between management and apprentices with a written agreement that the former should train the latter over a given period. During the 1930s slump apprentices were kept on in some shipyards when all journeymen had been paid off and a ship was known to have been built entirely by foremen and apprentices. In 1960 there had been a Clyde shipyards apprentices' strike which was particularly regretted by the employers. This strike for better wages, unfortunately led by one of our apprentices Dick Douglas, destroyed that bond. The young started to be paid more than they were worth, a trend which has continued so that forty years later young people throughout Britain appear to have priced themselves out of the market.

Since becoming Managing Director my job had become extremely stressful, but yacht racing provided a vital escape during the summer months. It was an intensely engrossing activity which occupied Saturdays and two evenings each week. While I was at University my Aunt Agnes Stephen kindly gave Jim and me her elderly Dragon Class yacht, a thirty foot three man keel boat of an Olympic Class. Though my forebears had excelled in international racing, I was totally inexperienced, so when I announced my intention to race, my mother exclaimed in horror "But Sandy – think of the family reputation!" From small beginnings progress was made and, having acquired a new Dragon, I entered her for the Olympic trials at Poole in the summer of 1968. Only one boat would be selected for the Mexico games the following year, and with Sue and Andrew Nicholson[1] as crew we joined the fleet of 31 contesting boats without any serious expectations. Our summer holiday turned out to be gruelling when the programme of seven races over testing 10 mile courses was extended to nine days because two races were abandoned as no boat managed to finish within the 5 hour time limit. On one of these we were leading, half a mile from the finishing line, when the time limit expired. With one race remaining we were delighted to be one of the four crews still contending for selection. To represent Britain at Acapulco would have been the experience of a lifetime but I could hardly abandon my stricken company for the months required for training and participation. In the end the best boat won, so we joined a queue to get our boat lifted out of the water and spent the night in our Land Rover towing the trailer so that I could be at Linthouse for a critical meeting next morning.

The Engineering Company was not helped by outsiders thinking it was closing as well as the Linthouse shipyard. The market for fabrications was at rock bottom in 1968, so work for the Boiler Shop was taken on at very low prices. In due course the market improved and so did the results of our sales effort where Tom Evans made several very good contacts. Spare space in the Engine Works was let out. For several years Scottish Curling Stones, whose granite came from Ailsa Craig, rented part of the Light Machine Shop. They were a part of the very successful Robertson Research, an offshoot of the

1. Andrew later married my sister Liz Denholm's daughter Jane.

Gem Line, and run by Jim Robertson, a family and yachting friend. After a number of years he suggested that we should take over Scottish Curling Stones. It was a most appealing proposition but an examination showed that we could not make curling stones at a competitive price. Sadly neither could they, so our happy relationship with the company ceased when they closed.

The Repair Company hit a problem. Ships under repair sometimes required new shell plates to be fitted and suitable plates had to be found, cut, bent to shape, welded into position and painted in a period which might be as little as two days. The Linthouse Platers' Shop had always met the repairing needs but when Linthouse and Fairfield steelwork organisations were amalgamated, their production and accounting became chaotic, and our ex-Platers' Shop became incapable of meeting Repair's requirements. The problem was solved largely at foreman level by transferring our custom to Connell's which, although a part of UCS, still had independence and they gave us an excellent service.

Shiprepairing accounting was unusual in that the best practice was to present the Owner's superintendent with his invoice before his ship sailed, as prompt invoicing usually meant prompt payment. The Engine Company accounting system had difficulty with this requirement but more importantly the need to concentrate all shiprepairing activities in one place became apparent as the ties with Linthouse lessened. A new office costing £20,000 was built at the Wet Basin and Denny McGuffie moved in with his management, office and accounting staff. In spite of having everything at the centre of operations getting out invoices before a ship left always remained a problem particularly when the workload was high. Now separated from the Shipyard, the Repair labour force had to be increased and small workshops were put up for plumbers, riggers and joiners.

The Repair Company employed between 250 and 400 men

and because we were not the Trade Unions' main target, we were able to avoid some of the strikes. However the ease with which the Unions twisted the tail of UCS had given them fresh confidence and they attacked us to match the UCS rates. The overtime obtainable by men involved in shiprepair made the work attractive and for a while we were able to keep our rates below those of UCS. However the Boilermakers' Union saw Government money pouring into UCS and were not interested in the fact that we never received a penny of Government assistance, so we were forced to keep up with the very high UCS rates. At the end of 1969 our boilermakers put on an overtime ban which affected voyage repairs really seriously. They wanted more money 'to achieve parity [with UCS] on account of the company's prosperity'. At that stage the Repair Company had lost almost £100,000 since being separated from the Shipyard. Some prosperity!

My brother Jim had the unenviable responsibility of looking after the three loss-making diversifications. Pitt Trailers had been making heavy losses and a serious fire at the works increased these losses dramatically. The plan had been to increase turnover to become profitable but the trailer venture was never able to achieve this. After a time it was decided to get rid of Pitts. This was not easy and it was eventually sold off to a management buyout, having cost us a huge amount of money.

The other two diversifications had very personable chief executives, both supreme optimists – a disastrous loss this year was always going to turn to profit next year, always 'jam tomorrow'. Hydel continued to market the drilling rig which had been designed at Linthouse but no orders for it were received and Robert Penney bought us out in 1969. We had to write off £70,000 development costs on top of the annual losses for the smallest of our diversifications.

The future in the container industry for ASCHE seemed less dismal and there were occasional times when we thought we might get some of tomorrow's jam, but it never happened. The Conjac straddle carrier was ideal for small container depots but large depots with stacked containers, for which the Conjac was unsuitable, was becoming the norm. Containers were standardising at 40 feet and Conjacs only catered for 20 and 30 feet. Watkins fought a hard battle to get finance for a 40 foot Conjac, but our Board rightly thought it too clumsy and that there would be little demand for it. ASCHE thereafter concentrated their business on tractors and the occasional Conjac but the losses continued after peaking at £65,000 one year. In 1971 the Company was sold to a management buyout in which Jim loyally remained involved.

Thus ended our disastrous attempts at diversification. Although the figures were never totalled, the losses over the years were substantially over £1,000,000. The diversifications brought no work whatsoever into the Engine Works or Shipyard. All this reinforced my view that a Shipyard was only suitable for building ships. Our only successful diversification had been the dredging business, a specialised type of shipbuilding.

The year to March 1969 showed a loss of £223,891 even though the Engine Company had somehow managed to make a small profit. Repair, with a much bigger task, had made a loss but the majority of the loss was due to diversifications. Jim had endured the stress of the last five horrific years and his health was suffering, so he resigned as Chairman. I made it clear that I was not the right person for his job and Robert Kemp took over. We never regretted his appointment, although Jim and I had many arguments with him and at times we hated his guts. Robert did what was required in a very effective way and without him the shareholders would have got little return. He was a great man for enumerating the points on which decisions had to be made; so much so that Watkins, the Chief Executive of ASCHE, referred to him privately as "Old one two three".

My efforts in separating our business from that of UCS were nearing completion, so Jim and I became Non-Executive

Directors although Jim continued to take an interest in ASCHE and I chaired Engineering and Repair Board meetings. In stepping down neither of us received a penny of compensation and even missed out on redundancy pay. At the time of writing my pension for my years at Linthouse is the princely sum of £2,200 a year. Jim and I were satisfied that one of our aims had been achieved in that virtually all our employees had kept their jobs. This yet again refuted Sean Connery's allegation, made in the Fairfield's film 'Bowlers and Bunnets', that when a shipyard closed the bosses walk away with all the money leaving the employees with nothing.

Humphrey Massey, the Financial Director, resigned and departed to the peace of Argyll to run the Crinan Boatyard where his wife ran a shop called the 'Boatique'. Tom Evans had joined the Main Board in 1969 and Ron Barclay, our Accountant, joined him later in the year. My father, who had taken no active part in the business for a number of years, finally resigned and it was sad that he, who had guided the Company so successfully for over 30 years, should see the near total destruction of his efforts.

The formation of UCS caused problems with dredgers as the normal split between ship and engine was inappropriate even though Simons Lobnitz (Engineering) was ultimately created to allow Engineering to operate the spares business. The merger agreement also left us owning the shell companies of Simons Lobnitz (Alluvial Dredges) and also Alluvial Dredges. Although we had built the tin dredger *Banka*, the possibility of future orders in this field looked remote, but surprisingly I became involved in a most unusual venture.

Long before Spain invaded Bolivia in the 16th century, a shepherd had been benighted near the top of the 16,000 high Potosi mountain. He lit a fire to keep himself from freezing and on raking the ashes in the morning was surprised to find shiny metal underneath which turned out to be pure silver. Millions of years ago a geological upheaval had created the most concentrated silver deposits ever known and the locals learned to use it to make their domestic utensils and other workaday items. When the Spaniards arrived they grabbed the silver and put the local population to work in the silver mines in the most appalling conditions and Potosi silver financed the Spanish Empire for centuries. The geological upheaval had also produced tin ore lower down the mountain which was mined until it gave out. Nature had washed tin ore into the local river where it gradually sank down through the mud to become concentrated just above the bedrock where it remained untouched for millions of years.

Two young Bolivian brothers Gonzalo and Antonio de Lozada surveyed the river bed and reckoned that the tin was recoverable. A dredger would have to be built in the river gorge 11,000 above sea level to work its way up river to 15,000 feet. The river was narrow and one short passage between rocks was hard to navigate. The gorge was remote and access not easy and combustion engines would have to be supercharged because of the thin air at high altitude. The brothers approached Alluvial Dredges and Jimmy Hamilton, although a UCS employee, helped to get the enquiry moving. Don Cross, a competent and able Englishman with tin dredging experience, joined the Stephen organisation and progressed the enquiry. Jimmy continued to help and some of the UCS ex-S.L. technical staff were also involved, operating in their spare time.

The Stephen Board was slightly taken aback at the thought of taking on such unusual work but agreed, as it seemed a sound proposition. We were to build a dredger complete, using our own labour – getting materials and machinery to site, building it and finally training the locals to operate it. Only the accommodation for our workers would be supplied by the Lozadas. The unknowns were tremendous, so our price included a healthy margin for error. Both Gonzalo and Antonio de Lozada (Gonny, a graduate of Yale and Tony of

Oxford) came over more than once to progress the enquiry. As they had no track record in the mining industry and, as Bolivia was somewhat volatile, their main problem was to satisfy Export Credits Guarantee Department to obtain credit. The problems were gradually overcome and the contract was signed. Don Cross set up a four man Drawing Office at Linthouse for the detailed design and ordering of materials, machinery, plant, diggers, vehicles etc. The dredger was to be all electric with power supplied from the local mains. There was some work for the Engine and Boiler shops at Linthouse but most of the material and machinery went directly from the manufacturer to the shipping port with steel for the hull being cut exactly to size and bent as required. We had to supply vehicles to transport everything from the railhead to the river gorge and a mobile crane for the building.

There were few logistical problems although some items had to be flown out to Bolivia. The casting for the bottom of the bucket ladder was found to be faulty when it was machined and had to be replaced, causing an unholy panic concerning the completion date, but a replacement was sent out to Bolivia by air just in time. Don flew to the port of Antafagasta in Chile, where materials and machinery were unloaded, to supervise their transfer from ship to railway and later from railway to site. At Antafagasta bags of cement on pallets were left in the open, ready for loading onto the train the following day. Don asked that they should be covered by a tarpaulin in case it rained but was met with a blank stare as nobody knew what a tarpaulin was. The locals told him that it had not rained at Antafagasta for 50 years. They were covered and that night it rained! Everything was carried up the Andes to the railhead in Bolivia on the Antafagasta Railways, still partly British owned. Our vehicles then took it all from there to the site and thereafter were used to transport our men between the camp and the building site.

Everything of importance arrived on time, which said a

great deal for Don's organisation, and building went as well as could be expected in unusual surroundings. The mains electricity was very unreliable with power cuts and voltage which dropped dramatically when the housewives in the nearby town started to cook their evening meal. Potosi Airport was essential for getting men and materials urgently required to the site. It consisted of a sloping field on which small planes landed uphill and took off downhill. The control tower was only manned when an aeroplane landed or took off. If an arrival was expected the Radio Operator was picked up from his home in Potosi and taken to the airport. He unlocked the control tower, cranked up the generator, started his radio and talked the plane in and, after it had taken off again, he was delivered back home. Occasionally an incoming plane had to buzz the airfield to remove a flock of grazing llamas.

The dredger was built on a shingle beach with a bund built round it to keep the water out in the wet season. Our team increased to 30 men as the structure took shape and the fitting out work got under way. The men were hand picked Glasgow shipyard workers of the necessary trades. Most had never been abroad before, but all worked splendidly. Demarcation, as practised by the Union dominated Clyde shipyards, was ignored. With no shop steward looking on, everybody was keen to help other trades and to learn their skills. Completion was three months later than planned but it was still a remarkable achievement. By the time the dredger was completed the de Lozada brothers were desperately short of cash so it was a great relief to them when the first batch of tin ore reached the market.

After the dredger had been working for a year we were horrified to hear that it had capsized and I flew out to see if we could help. At the same time an expert from the Salvage Association arrived who in due course declared the dredger to be a 'total constructive loss'. Lloyds of London paid out in full and the de Lozada brothers bought the capsized dredge and set about reinstating it. The biggest problem was with the electric motors which had been underwater for some time so they were baked until all the moisture had been removed. Luckily no rewinding was required as the fresh water had done surprisingly little damage. Once the motors had been rectified, the dredger became operative again surprisingly quickly. In the meantime John Robson, Stephen's Technical Director who had retired, but remained on the Board as a Non-Executive, checked the stability of the dredger and found that the Simons Lobnitz Naval Architect, who had done the calculations while moonlighting from UCS, had missed out the weight of the steel deck from his calculations, so the stability was not what it should have been. I had been unaware that a bucket dredger could become unstable if the bucket chain is lowered and pressed hard on the bed. To improve the stability, camels (flotation tanks) were bolted onto each side of the hull, to be removed only when the dredger was working its way through the narrow passage between the rocks. There was no trouble after that and our final profit on the contract was over £80,000. It must have also have been successful for the de Lozada brothers as many years later Gonny became President of Bolivia and was re-elected for a second term. He should have been a very good President but things went wrong for him in his second term and, after being hounded out of office, he moved to the USA.

The only 'knock-down'[2] ship Stephen's had built previously was a 70 ton schooner *Aurora del Titicaca* in 1869 for Lake Titicaca in the Andes where we carried out an operation similar to that of the tin dredger. In those days there had been no railway so no part of the ship could weigh more than 150 pounds which was the most a mule could carry. It is an

2. A knock-down ship is one which is designed and partly assembled in a shipyard, then dismantled and shipped to its destination for final construction – a floating version of a present day Ikea flatpack.

extraordinary coincidence that the only two 'knock-down' vessels built by Stephen's should have finished up on the other side of the world within 400 miles of each other. When *Aurora* was being built, two steamships were already operating on Lake Titicaca, so it might appear surprising that the Peruvians reverted to sail. Transporting coal from the coast by mule was prohibitively expensive and there were no trees to provide fuel. The steamships had been fuelled by dried llama dung, and it seems that they couldn't produce enough for a third ship.

At Linthouse the separation of the Shipyard was gradually completed. The computer department was an anomaly in that the building and the computer belonged to us but the operators were UCS employees. When they got a new computer we sold them the building and sold the old computer which didn't fetch a great deal. The Recreation Club had lost its base as most of its members were now with UCS. As a groundsman could no longer be afforded the sports activities had to be shut down, but the social club continued until the property was sold in 1971 to the Southern General Hospital for £135,000[3]. Most of the Stephen Boys' Club members had become UCS employees but the building in Cressy Street still belonged to us so it was sold to them.

In the year to March 1970 Alexander Stephen & Sons showed a profit of £29,947, the first surplus for several years. Engineering was profitable but Repair made a loss due to a dock strike and labour troubles. Alluvial Dredges made a good contribution but ASCHE continued to drag us down. The following year was slightly better with a profit of £40,889. This time Repair had had a very successful year but Engineering and ASCHE both lost money. We started to have trouble getting financial matters settled with UCS. Payment for work done was agreed, but they failed to produce invoices for their work and about the middle of 1970 it became clear that UCS

3. Almost £1,700.000 today.

had a serious cash shortage. We could not risk allowing them to build up any debt, even though the Government was expected to bail them out. When *HMS Hermione*, which had become a UCS ship, was being drydocked by us, we considered keeping her there until some of our bills were settled but decided it would be counter-productive. However we briefly impounded their lorry fleet which was still garaged on our property. Tony Hepper blew his top but our action had some effect. All this put Jim in an awkward position as a Director of UCS and he resigned in 1970.

In June 1971 UCS went into liquidation. Their being in trouble was no surprise but everybody had expected the Government to rescue them. However Edward Heath's Conservative Government took a tough line which caused much financial distress among UCS's subcontractors and suppliers. Due to Stephen's skilful operation, UCS only owed us £3,700, but Repair owed almost £50,000 and Engineering was owed a similar sum. According to a strict interpretation of the law, Engineering and Repair were separate companies and there could be no offset. We were struggling for money at the time and the loss of £50,000 would have been serious. However the Liquidator, Robert Smith yet again, took a sensible view and treated the two as one entity. As we had already written off our investment in UCS, their closure had no direct financial effect, but we lost a most important customer who had been providing Engineering with a steady stream of work and Repair with drydockings. It was another nail in our coffin. I was sorry for the UCS Chairman Tony Hepper who had accepted a poisoned chalice. Despite the confrontation to save our company, he was someone with whom I could have got on well, but he was never a shipbuilder.

The detailed reasons for UCS's insolvency never emerged. When a Liquidator is appointed, it is not his job to spend time and money analysing the cause of his appointment. Employees likewise look to their futures and put the past behind them.

Having inherited a complex situation, UCS made catastrophic losses in a surprisingly short time. Yarrow's and Connell's had profitable order books and could not have contributed to the losses, Brown's *Queen Elizaeth 2* turned out much as expected so there could not have been much loss there and Stephen's ships should have produced a profit with minimal run down costs due to other yards being able to absorb the labour force. Certainly UCS had their tail twisted by the Unions and their organisation left much to be desired but these four yards could not have been responsible for any great loss. UCS's cataclysmic losses must have come from elsewhere. Fairfield's took on orders at prices well below those offered by other British yards and they achieved no increase in productivity. Thus UCS's losses must have been caused largely by Fairfield's contracts. At the time of the UCS merger negotiations, these effects should have become apparent.

Nine months after UCS had gone into liquidation, the South of Scotland Electricity Board suddenly realised that our Engine Company was being supplied by UCS and that they might not receive what we had paid UCS for our electricity. SSEB panicked and threatened to cut us off, but with the help of the Liquidator the matter was resolved.

CHAPTER 15
On Our Own, 1972–75

Life's but a walking shadow – MacBeth

The 'Work In', staged by the employees of UCS when their jobs were threatened, surprised everybody. It was a unique industrial action controlled by the shop stewards Jimmy Airlie and Sammy Barr of Fairfield's while the highly effective orator Jimmy Reid of Brown's gave them publicity throughout Britain. The Unions could only look on in amazement while Robert Smith, the Liquidator, handled it brilliantly. Eventually the Conservative Government, whose original plan had been to let the whole outfit go to the wall, responded to public feeling generated by the Work In, and Fairfield's and Connell's were reprieved to become Govan Shipbuilders.

Stephen's was not involved and we soldiered on alone. Our Engineering Company obtained several contracts for Sperry designed ships' stabilisers which included a shell plate, shaped and cut to fit into the hull of the ship. This was a good product for the works but it was only a subcontract, as was most of our work, and we were up against competition from Italy and Japan. Fife Forge was another customer with whom we built up a good relationship and we machined many tail shafts for them. Large pressure vessels for power stations and oil refineries, mostly for Motherwell Bridge Engineering, kept the Boilershop employed and our proximity to King George V Dock for shipping was in our favour. To bend plates for pressure vessels an elderly machine was brought back into play but the plates were thicker than those previously rolled so its hydraulic pipes had to be replaced, but when repaired it bent plates more accurately if somewhat slower than the modern machines. We also obtained contracts for air circulators, gear cases, compressor parts and other bits of machinery and the Engineering Company's workforce increased to 475. G & J Weir leased a substantial area of the works to fabricate their pressure vessels. Manufacturing granite rolls for papermaking machinery was another sideline which went well until the paper industry went into a severe recession and the work dried up. Being a smaller organisation, the Unions did not trouble Engineering too much and we had a good labour relationship, but wage rates were always a problem as they were driven upwards by our more prosperous or subsidised neighbours. We still had to put up with the occasional strike. The battle between the Ted Heath's Government and the Trade Unions in the 'Winter of Discontent' in 1973 had a serious effect when we had to cut our production down to three days a week due to electricity rationing.

As our light machines were out of date, work concentrated on the Heavy Machine Shop where the machinery was relatively modern except that we had no milling capacity. As soon as Stephen's broke even, we bought two milling machines but, to pay for them, we had to sell the underused Craven crankshaft lathe. The day after the Craven had been sold, an unexpected order for the lathe came in, closely followed by several others. As the purchaser was a broker and had not found a customer we rented it back to undertake these profitable orders. All heavy machines had to work double shifts to pay their way. Our problem was that our turnover was largely subcontract work which was vulnerable in a recession when our customers had very little to subcontract.

Our patternmakers, cut down to three in 1968, now only repaired wooden patterns required to make castings for our spares business, and, when a new pattern was wanted, its manufacture was subcontracted. The Aircraft Store, as soon as it had been vacated by UCS, was turned into an effective Pattern Store with a small Pattern Shop in the same area. The Pattern Shop, east of Holmfauld Road, had been rented out but the store remained empty. In 1973 the whole area, for which we now had no need, was sold to Govan Shipbuilders whose principal requirement was for a car park.

Fleming and Ferguson of Paisley's last ship sailed down the River Cart in 1969, but Alf Player, their ex-Managing Director continued as a consultant. We built up a good relationship with him and supplied him with almost all the parts for a bucket dredger for Sri Lanka and also worked with him on several other projects, eventually taking over the Fleming and Fergusson spares business which gave us a good turnover. On our own we landed an order for a 'knock-down' bucket dredger for the Bombay Port Trust which was put together by their local labour, but it was in fact the last ship to be built by Stephen's.

The Engine Company had installed its own do-it-yourself telephone exchange and a clerkess answered incoming calls. It worked well but I missed the friendly voices of the two switchboard operators who had been transferred to UCS in 1968. Five years later I wanted to get in touch with Archie Gilchrist who was Managing Director of Govan Shipbuilders. I dialled the number and asked "Could I speak to Mr Gilchrist?" and was promptly answered "Certainly Mr Sandy" by Mrs Patrick who had manned our exchange. A good telephonist could do wonders for a company.

The Repair Company absorbed Scottish Lion, a small Glasgow based ship repair company whose turnover was largely for their owners, Clan Line whose ships were shortly to abandon the river. Most of the Scottish Lion labour force was taken on including their Managing Director, Tom Stewart, whose experience was very useful. Repair undertook major contracts for the Ministry of Defence and merchant shipping companies at very keen prices, as these enabled us to avoid 'down time'. However keeping the men continually employed was always a problem. One morning Denny McGuffie told me that in two days' time we would have 200 men on the books and no prospect of work for them, but he rang me that evening to say that an emergency job had just come in and he would be short of labour. We were not often as lucky as that. In 1974 Barclay Curle Shiprepairing Company closed. This did little to help us as their business was primarily long term contracts and they undertook few voyage repairs, but when their neighbours, Yarrow's, took over their property we lost the drydocking for Naval work.

One of the most controversial contracts obtained by Repair was the completion of the UCS ship *Alisa* where the Liquidator had problems in getting it finished with UCS labour. The Unions were co-operative and the contract went well but offers to finish two other UCS ships came to nothing, largely for political reasons. In 1971 we were pleased to welcome home *Sir Galahad* for a refit. Even though we were short of turnover there were two unusual ships which we worked on with little profit. The old sailing clipper *Carrick* was moored in Glasgow at Clyde Street and housed the RNVR Club. Her wooden hull was rotten in places and the painters had to be careful not to put their paintbrushes through the planks. They swore that the ship only survived because 'the woodworms were holding hands'[1]. The Clyde paddle steamer *Waverley* was always in need of repair and we worked on her for very low prices as an act of charity. A badly needed new boiler could not be afforded so regular patching was essential. Forty years later *Waverley*, with a new boiler, still provides pleasure trips round the coast of Britain.

The three old Govan Drydocks, owned and run by the

1. *Carrick* sank on her way to be drydocked in 1991 but was salvaged and taken to the Scottish Maritime Museum for restoration. After much work had been done on her, the funding ran out and she sat in Irvine for years. In 2014 the City of Adelaide (her original name) took her over and transported her to Australia so the woodworms must have tightened their grip.

Clyde Port Authority, were essential to the Repair business. No. 1 dock was more or less redundant, but Nos. 2 and 3 were effective and all ships built at Linthouse, except the 50,000 ton tanker *British Bombardier* whose beam was too great, had been drydocked there. By 1971 the Port Authority was losing money on the docks due to shrinking demand, so a formula was agreed whereby we took over the operating of the docks as well as their staff of 13. We were able to employ the men largely on other work and we became more competitive for long repair contracts.

Even after UCS had gone into liquidation, the Unions forced up labour rates to match those of Govan Shipbuilders. Strikes were less frequent, but still occurred, and were usually timed to cause maximum disruption. Sometimes the strike which upset us was remote as on one disastrous occasion when two good long term refit contracts were cancelled at the last minute, costing us about £50,000, because of a dock strike on the Mersey.

The Repair Company became profitable but the underlying trend was not good. Every year the number of ships coming to the Clyde decreased, often as much as 20%. Container ships now came to Greenock to unload and reload in three days. Most of Britain's trade was now with the Continent so shipping focused on the East Coast. When we quoted for conversions and major overhauls the ships had to come from the East or South Coast and the cost of bringing them to the Clyde put us at a disadvantage.

In the early 1970s North Sea oil had tremendous growth possibilities and related work was sought by Engineering with little success. For shiprepairing the East Coast now appeared a better option than the West so we set up a small operation at Grangemouth which, after a year, moved to Leith where Alexander Stephen (Forth) Ltd. obtained voyage repairs and dry docking. Minimal losses were recorded for the first two years but the conversion of a dredger was then taken on where our organisation proved to be inadequate and a court case resulted, the only litigation in my time at Stephen's. We won our case. The Forth operation was down-graded but after that more or less broke even. The decision to start shiprepairing on the Forth had been a brave one, but the increase in traffic did not match our expectations as North Sea Oil focussed on Aberdeen.

Alluvial Dredges was not fitting into the Stephen scheme and was ultimately sold to Jimmy Hamilton and Don Cross in a management buyout.

Stephen's had put in a first class Staff Pension Scheme in 1950 but with no provision for inflation, which later became normal. At the same time we set up a non-contributory scheme for hourly paid employees with over 30 years service, the first of its kind in Clydeside heavy industry with tradesmen receiving £1 a week[2]. Due to lack of profit in the 1960s we were not in a position to improve these schemes. When UCS put in an up-to-date scheme, we were outgunned but could do nothing until our position had stabilised, so it was 1973 before we introduced a modern pension scheme which was, of course, more expensive. It could do nothing for retired staff who had lost out badly in times of rampant inflation. The pension of one foreman who had retired in 1958 was only worth 13% of what it had been when he retired. Alexander Stephen & Sons could not help but the independent Stephen Bicentenary Trust could. This Trust was set up by my father in 1950 when he donated £1,200 to add to the £10,000 put up by the Company. The simple Trust Deed, assisted 'employees and ex-employees or their families in straitened or penurious circumstances'. David Fullarton, the Personnel Manager, managed the handouts and, as the income was not fully spent, grants of £20 a year were given to retired employees with between 20 and 30 years service. The Trust absorbed one or two small funds such

2. £30 today.

as Miss E M Stephen's Prize Fund, set up my great-aunt Elsie, Fred's sister, to help impecunious apprentices from the Highlands. My father invested the Trust capital in equities and managed the portfolio brilliantly. The good investment performance continued after I took over in 1964 and thus the capital became substantial.

At the time of the merger the responsibility for paying pensions to our long service pensioners from the shipyard was transferred to UCS while we continued to pay those who had worked for Engineering and Repair. When UCS went bust, their pensioners were left high and dry, but the Trust came to the rescue and also took on the Engineering and Repair obligations even though it meant overspending the Trust income. Jim and I were determined that no pensioner should be deprived and were prepared to contribute personally if necessary. Because I was a Non-Executive Director of Scottish Widows Life Assurance Company I had access to their life expectancy tables and was relieved when my calculations showed that the Trust could meet all its obligations leaving most of the £180,000[3] capital for future use.

Stephen's came up against an asset stripper of the worst kind who bought up ordinary shares for himself and his clients and, when he controlled 15%, campaigned to close the company down and grab the assets. He failed to understand that heavy engineering was a long term business and that, unless a company was closed in the right way and at the right time, all the assets would be lost. As he refused to come to Glasgow, Robert Kemp had to spend a lot of time visiting him and dealing with his convoluted and often libellous letters as he simply wanted to get his hands on the money which appeared in our accounts. The Asset Stripper was even offered a seat on the Board but he refused and continued to waste a huge amount of Robert Kemp's and the Board's time. Other

3. £1,800,000 today.

takeover approaches from people who were primarily interested in our tax losses or our stock market quotation gradually fizzled out.

Jim and I now did little more than attend board meetings. I was deeply worried to see my brother's health deteriorate but he continued to do valiant work for Linthouse and Govan Housing Associations. I was fortunate to have my Scottish Widows directorship and expand my involvement with Murray Johnstone's investment trusts. I also took over a small company, Polymer Scotland, which was to carry out concrete repairs and specialist work with epoxy resin including re-laying the helicopter flight decks of Royal Fleet Auxiliaries, amongst whose numbers were *Sir Galahad* and *Sir Geraint*. At the end of 1973 Denny McGuffie retired but continued as a Non-Executive Director for a year. He had created a viable shiprepairing outfit when some would have deemed it impossible. McGuffie was succeeded by Fred Adam who had been with Repair for many years and with whom I had worked in the Ship Drawing Office. The following year Tom Evans retired from running the Engineering Company. He too had achieved marvels in difficult circumstances. Adam Thomson was appointed in his stead. He was a younger man with a more scientific approach who improved the planning and organisation. Although the Dredger Section was closed down, the profitable spares turnover of £250,000 continued. This was a small part of our business but the only part we owned, all the rest being subcontract work. A recession in heavy engineering was on the way so the outlook was not good, particularly for subcontractors.

Stephen's had owned the finest collection of ship paintings of any British shipyard. Shipping companies displayed portraits or models of their flagships but when the ship was sold they were replaced. What they discarded had helped us to build up a collection which included four oil paintings by George Napier and three by William Clark, who had been the top marine artists in the second half of the nineteenth century when ships' portraits were much in vogue. The biggest, was Napier's *Shenandoah*[4] built at Kelvinhaugh in 1863 from where the ship had been delivered to a Liverpool owner as *Sea King*, but went on to become a notorious Confederate raider in the American Civil War. For six months after the Confederates had surrendered, *Shenandoah* continued her quest to sink Yankee ships, while ignoring protestations that the war had ended.

In the 1950s a painting of *Clyde*[5], an East Indiaman built in 1860, by William Clark was added to the collection, having been spotted in the window of a London art gallery by the Shipyard Chief Draughtsman John Stevenson. Afterwards he asserted that Clark had painted the rigging incorrectly. Between 1930 and 1958 we commissioned ten paintings from Bernard Gribble and also displayed some fine models but, as there was limited space in our offices, most models of our ships went to museums and can still be seen all round the world. As a small boy I remember being taken to visit the model maker at Linthouse. He was a very old man and after he retired, all model-making was subcontracted.

When the UCS merger was being negotiated Jim and I were more concerned about the jobs of 3,500 employees than about pictures and consequently accepted the agreement which allocated our pictures and models to UCS. At that time we thought the future of UCS was more assured than our remaining organisation, but we were wrong and should have insisted on keeping the pictures as they had no value recorded in the books. After UCS's insolvency the paintings by Napier and Clark were auctioned by Sotheby's at Gleneagles Hotel. Brother Jim, cousin David, sister Liz and I formed a ring to buy back some of them, which was probably illegal. My choice was *John Lidgett*[6] by William Clark, a composite

4. Plate 45.
5. Plates 43 and 44.
6. Plate 57.

sailing ship[7] built in 1862. The painting had been commissioned by Stephen's and showed two other ships built by us in the background. It was first to be auctioned and the price went beyond my top figure of £3,500. We were devastated but thereafter the ring worked well and we each got a painting. The seven paintings fetched over £30,000[8] in total. *Shenandoah*, which was too big and too highly valued for the family, was sold for £11,000 and changed hands again in 1985 for £44,000.

Twenty five years later Sue and I were staying with friends on Speyside and were invited to Sunday lunch at Tulchan Lodge near Grantown-on-Spey. As the house was known to have some good paintings, the conversation turned to the pictures and I related the story of how I had failed to buy *John Lidgett*. After lunch we were taken round the collection when, at the top of the stairs, I could hardly believe my eyes as *John Lidgett* was straight in front of me. The dealer who bought it at Gleneagles had sold it to the owner of Tulchan Lodge who had previously hung it in his fishing lodge on the Isle of Harris. The painting changed hands again in 2001 for £55,000 – beyond my pocket for the second time.

Robert Smith, the Liquidator of UCS still held our less valuable paintings, but I was able to buy back eight of them for £600. Of most interest was *Cyphrenes*[9], a Dundee built steamship of 1872, which had been owned by the Stephen family. She had a special family connection because my great-great-uncle Samuel Stephen was Master. On the ship's maiden voyage from Dundee to Plymouth a tragedy occurred when he was accidentally washed overboard and drowned. His newly married wife, who had been on board with him and was

7. A composite ship had a wooden hull and iron frames with diagonal iron strapping to give exceptional strength. The technique had been patented by the Young Alexander Stephen.
8. £350,000 today.
9. Plate 56.

expecting their first child, came ashore at Plymouth a widow. She was later given the painting by her father-in-law and Samuel's posthumous daughter kindly presented it back to the Company in 1949. I am fortunate to have it hanging in my dining room at the time of writing.

A magnificent model of *Viceroy of India*[10] was given to us by P & O after the ship had been sunk during World War II. The model was in an Engineering Company office when UCS was formed and we offered to house it until they found a suitable place, but it was removed immediately. A week later I was horrified to find it dumped outside at the mercy of the elements and there it remained for some time despite my urgent pleas. Five years later Tony Browning an ex-Denny's man and Marine Curator of the Kelvingrove Museum and Art Gallery, which had been given the model when UCS went bust, showed me what I can only describe as 'chust a remains'[11]. It would take two thousand manhours to repair it and the Museum did not have the funds at the time. In 1985 I visited the Transport Museum which had taken over the marine side of Kelvingrove Museum, and was astonished to see the *Viceroy*, beautifully repaired, holding pride of place in their new display. The Transport Museum has now been replaced by the Riverside Museum where Glasgow's shipbuilding industry has been downplayed and the Clyde's magnificent history does not receive the recognition it deserves.

Ships lines, which define the shape of the hull, are now faired[12] by computers but when I was a shipbuilder it was done on a drawing board. In former times a Naval Architect designed the shape of each hull by carving a half block model. It was then dismantled for half widths to be measured and drawn out full size in the Mould Loft. Old half block models

10. Plate 59.
11. Quoted from *Para Handy* by Neil Munro.
12. Made fair, ensuring that the shape of the hull has no irregularities.

had been mounted on teak backboards and used to decorate the walls in the Directors' Lunchroom in the Main Office. As this area became UCS property, I had put them out of my mind. A year later my ex-colleague, the Head Foreman Joiner John Cairns, told me that over forty half models had been taken down and some had been stolen leaving the remainder uncared for. I studied the Sale Agreement, for the nth time, and decided that we had as much right to them as UCS, so with John's connivance I led a raiding party into UCS territory, loaded the half models onto a lorry and brought them back to our side of the Iron Curtain. Tony Browning, curator of the Kelvingrove Museum, was most helpful and was given those of special interest. We gave the Ben Line two models of their ships and a Clan Line model was given to the Cayser family to help start a museum while the remainder were put into store. We had no long term plan for them so they were later sold for about £200 each and I hope they still give pleasure to their owners.

CHAPTER 16

The Inevitable End, 1975–83

The last syllable of recorded time – MacBeth

In the second half of 1975 the recession in heavy industry deepened and Alexander Stephen Engineering's customers had little surplus to subcontract. Adam Thomson and his team strove valiantly to fill the shops but work was not forthcoming and our forward load shrank. He advised the Board that he could see no profitable future and the decision was taken to cease production. Some contracts would take over a year to fulfil so it was a slow run down. One contract was for variable pitch propeller shafting for warships being built at Thorneycroft, where the last pair were delivered on time mid 1976, more than four years after the order had been placed. An agreement on the run down was made with the labour force who co-operated well. As the work ran out, machine tools, the most valuable items on the books, were sold, all fetching substantially more than book value.

The closure of Engineering was a yet another blow to Repair though it was not mortal and some smaller machines were transferred to the Wet Basin to improve the 'in house' machining capacity. The Repair Company, having had a very profitable period, was in the doldrums again as the number of ships coming to the Clyde continued to fall. In the summer of 1976 a caulker was dismissed for drunkenness and a dozen of his mates walked out in sympathy. The dispute should have been quickly settled but the Boilermakers' Union did not help and the strike escalated. As there were no long term contracts under way, the whole labour force was then suspended. This should have brought the boilermakers to their senses, but their strike continued and, as we could see no long term future for Shiprepairing, we reluctantly called in the Receiver. The ubiquitous Robert Smith filled the position and it was a clean operation as the work was completed in a few weeks with most of his time spent on settlement of outstanding invoices. The premises were sold to the newly formed Clyde Dock Engineering who had persuaded the Unions to agree to greatly increased flexibility between trades, a 'no strike' agreement and reduced labour rates. These new conditions made considerable savings and they were successful for a few years, but they suffered from the market problems which had beset us, and eventually closed. Robert Smith did his usual efficient job in winding up Alexander Stephen Shiprepairers with all the creditors being paid in full, and about £50,000 returned to the Parent Company.

Normally Trade Unions negotiated favourable conditions for their members when a company closed down, but on this occasion there was no run down. They pursued Robert Smith for money without success and then demanded that the Stephen Parent Company should make them ex-gratia payments. I met a large Union committee on my own and heard their case which I refuted. They then suggested that the Stephen family shareholders should brass up. My reply was that, while shareholders' money had supported Repair for ten years getting virtually no dividends, the Boilermakers had destroyed the Company by their irresponsible action and so it was they who should make an ex-gratia payment to the shareholders. That was the last time I met with Trade Unionists.

Stephen Board Meetings became fewer with less to discuss. I was lucky in having built a new career and was fully occupied in my spare time as Sue and I had moved to Ballindalloch near Balfron where we became involved in considerable manual labour while knocking off 25 rooms to create a manageable house[1]. Jim was less lucky as his marriage had ended when he and his wife divorced in 1980. He continued to live peacefully at his home in the West End of Glasgow and devoted his time to much needed charitable work.

The Institution of Engineers and Shipbuilders had played an important part in the shipbuilding industry. Every year five or six technical papers attracted a cross section of members from managing directors to junior draughtsmen. These events were a great opportunity for young men to make an impression on the top brass by asking intelligent questions during the discussion. Being multidisciplinary it attracted civil engineers, academics and others with engineering interests. The Institution hosted the prestigious 'James Watt Dinner' annually which was attended by over 600 members and their guests and was always oversubscribed. The first Institution paper I attended was in 1943 when as a teenager I listened to my father giving his Presidential Address on ships' tonnage. I understood little of the contents but was proud to be there. I became an irregular attender and was rather surprised when asked to join the Council after I had stopped being a shipbuilder. When Jim Turner of John Brown Engineering became President and I had been elected Vice President, the Institution was losing money at a considerable rate. Burlington House, our large headquarters in Bath Street, was sold and the full time Secretary retired. Modest office space was rented with a room available for meetings while a member became part time Secretary with continuity being maintained by Doris Callaghan in the office. The money from the sale of Burlington House was invested after I had persuaded the Council to buy equities rather than gilt edged stock, a decision which has put the Institution into a strong position. The funds were well managed by a partner of the stockbrokers Speirs and Jeffrey, Jim Gibb, who

1. Recorded in *The Lost History of Ballindalloch – Balfron* by A M M & S M O Stephen.

later joined the Council and did stalwart work there as Treasurer.

I became President in 1983 and served the customary two years. There were occasions when I was out of my depth on the technical side but at least the financial side was sound. As President I attended several dinners including one given by the Deacon Convenor of the Trades House of Glasgow, an event which was attended by the great and good of Scotland. When I complained that my title 'President of the Institution of Engineers and Shipbuilders in Scotland' must be the longest of those at the dinner, an examination of the guest list revealed that 'The Moderator of the General Assembly of the Church of Scotland' was exceeded by one letter. The Institution, still active and financially healthy, now rents their office from Clydeport in Robertson Street where technical papers are presented in one of the most beautiful rooms in Scotland.

No satisfactory offer was received for the Linthouse land and buildings so we decided to make what we could of our facilities. While Engineering was running down, John Brown Engineering had taken a three year lease of two bays to erect and test their larger gas turbines. There was also plenty of space available for short lets and for storage while our lucrative spares business turned over £250,000 per annum. Thus Alexander Stephen & Sons became profitable to the tune of about £25,000 to £50,000 a year and we waited for a decent offer for our property to emerge. A staff of 15 kept the premises secure and carried on the spares business. Ron Barclay, previously Secretary and Director of Alexander Stephen & Sons, also became Managing Director and sole Accountant and, with little work-in-progress, our bank balance grew. Our new-found wealth allowed us to buy in the Preference Shares after back dividends had been paid off, and we then repaid the Ordinary Shareholders 24p of their 25p shares, the most we could pay while continuing to trade. Our Ordinary Shares had reached a peak of 62.5p in April 1965 but during the UCS years they languished between 13p and 17p. True to form, the Asset Stripper made a perfect nuisance of himself. He wanted *all* his money *now* and was not prepared to accept that the law did not permit this. When we eventually gave him what he had been demanding, there was not a word of thanks from this greedy man.

In the old part of the Works there were problems with the roofs which were constantly in need of repair but, as the future was uncertain, repair costs were kept to the minimum. Letting storage space was mostly for short periods, and usually at short notice, but a large area was let to Metal Box who stored millions of beer cans. The spares business thrived and Ron Barclay visited India, Pakistan, Bangladesh, Burma, Iraq and Egypt obtaining orders in most places. These countries were short of foreign exchange and often could not afford all that they needed. An order from Iraq was lost because Ron had come straight from Egypt and at that time the two countries were not on speaking terms.

At the end of their lease John Brown Engineering decided that they needed our premises long term and offered to buy the whole property and the spares business for £320,000. After this agreement was concluded in 1982, there was nothing to prevent Alexander Stephen & Sons Limited from being wound up. Ordinary shareholders were paid 32.85 pence the next year, in addition to the 24 pence they had already received, not far short of the 1965 peak of 62.5 pence but, because of inflation the two were not comparable. Having met all obligations Alexander Stephen & Sons Limited went into liquidation in early 1983. The final result fully justified our decision to continue Engineering and Repair without the shipyard. We had given employment to over 600 people for eight years and the shareholders came out better than they would have done if we had closed in 1968. The merchant banker's fees in connection with the UCS merger had been the only subsidy we ever got. After the merger, Engineering and Repair sought any likely assistance but never got a penny. However we had been able to shape our future independently and sensibly, although, while we had slogged away, we watched Governments pour fruitless millions into UCS and Govan Shipbuilders.

After the closure of the Engineering and Repair Companies, the Stephen Bicentenary Trust had only to provide pensions for a known number of long service people, but setting the levels was difficult. The Trust's Ordinary Shares were sold and dated gilt edged shares bought to allow more accurate calculations. I put forward a proposal with a relatively high life expectancy. My cousin David Stephen, also a Trustee, suggested that due to a history of smoking and drinking, Glaswegians lived less long than the national average, but satisfactory levels were worked out. A substantial surplus was revealed so we took on all long service Linthouse Shipyard people who had been transferred to UCS and a few staff who had been hard it by inflation, bringing the total on our books to 220. The pensions were greater than they had been at any time in the past and also allowed for inflation, while long service employees who just missed the cut were given a £150 retirement gift. After I had moved my office to Paisley, pensions were paid by a posted cheque. One labourer 'Big John' was a fine figure of a man who had worked all his life at Linthouse in spite of being deaf and dumb. He wanted nothing to do with cheques and when aged almost 80 he would walk the 6 miles from Govan to Paisley to collect his pension in cash. He accepted a cuppa in the office but had difficulty giving an up-to-date address in Govan. One year he failed to turn up and in spite of extensive enquiries I never learned what became of him.

Every Christmas I wrote a personal note to be sent with a cheque and a copy of the 'Linthouse News'. The contact could mean as much as the money and after a pensioner's death I regularly received a letter of thanks from the family. Latterly I ran the Trust from home and in 2002, with fewer than 20 beneficiaries, cousin David, eight years younger than me, took over. Not long after that the Merchants' House of Glasgow, who had pensioners of their own, took over the operation so that Stephen pensioners who outlived us would be secure. At the beginning of 2014 there were only four pensioners left though I could have qualified as a fifth. David had worked in the Personnel Office at Linthouse and was in Shipyard Planning, when he was transferred to UCS in 1968. He soon left to set up in business on his own account and ran 'Topstaff' successfully, supplying temporary office staff, chefs, lorry drivers and many others. Sadly David died in 2012.

From 1950 onwards the *Linthouse News* had been the Stephen works magazine consisting of 4 pages published monthly. It fulfilled its purpose well but I was not involved personally at that time. When the UCS merger took place it was discontinued but ten years later I reconstituted the publication for our pensioners. They wrote in with news. There were items about our ships. Shipbuilding stories were repeated and, of course, details of new pensioners and deaths were printed so producing four pages was no problem. It became clear that the *Linthouse News* was passed round the Govan pubs, hopefully earning our pensioners a few free drinks.

In 1982 Logistic Support Ships, *Sir Galahad* in particular, played a vital role in the Falklands War. When the shortage of helicopters had stalled the momentum of the British advance from Goose Green to Stanley, *Sir Galahad*[2] and *Sir Tristram* were loaded with troops and equipment and sailed to Bluff Cove ahead of the advancing troops on land. Because the shore in the Cove was unsuitable for landing ramps, the ships anchored and began to ferry everything ashore using their boats. When the weather cleared unexpectedly, they became visible to the enemy on the surrounding hills and Argentine aircraft from the mainland targeted the defenceless ships. *Sir*

2. Plate 69.

Galahad took the brunt of the attack as she was anchored in the most vulnerable position. The Welsh Guards and the ship's crew suffered horrific casualties from bombs and exploding ammunition and the ship was set on fire. Having been almost destroyed, the burned out vessel was later towed out to sea and scuttled.

Before *Galahad* was built, I had overseen the estimate, finalised the tender and posted it at the Glasgow Head Post Office at 9.30 p.m. to meet the Ministry of Defence deadline the following day. Then, when her engine suppliers had taken up weeks of my time, her delayed delivery caused sleepless nights. I made a speech at her launch and spent long hours on her bridge during her trials. She was refitted by our Shiprepair Company in 1973 and my small company, Polymer Scotland, later resurfaced her helicopter flight deck. In no other ship had I been so involved. Her death throes were broadcast world wide and I first became aware of the tragedy when I switched on my television and saw the flames leaping from her bridge. *Sir Galahad* had been part of my life and I mourned her loss deeply.

Epilogue

Shortly shall my labours end – The Tempest

Alexander Stephen & Sons' 233 years of history did not end when the shareholders were repaid and Linthouse built ships still plied the oceans. By now most Stephen ships have come to a natural or unnatural end, but a surprising number are still afloat. The oldest known survivor is the 112 ton steam yacht *Medea*[1]. In May 1904 Captain William Macallister Hall of Torrisdale on the Mull of Kintyre decided that the shooting season would be improved if his guests were transported by sea. Thus we designed and built *Medea* for him in 49 working days – an achievement that modern technology could not equal. In his declining years Macallister Hall was said to use his yacht to voyage down the coast to Campbelltown to visit his barber.

Medea was bought in 1914 by my great-great-uncle John Stephen and when he died in 1917 she was taken over by the French Navy to distinguish herself in anti-submarine work and later in minesweeping. She was bought in 1930 by my grandfather Fred Stephen, who had designed her and supervised her building and it was the third time she had been in Stephen hands. Fred had retired from being a successful amateur yacht racing helmsman and now wanted something more comfortable. He cruised the West Highlands each summer and my brother Jim, in his childhood, was lucky sometimes to be a passenger. The ship was prone to roll and on one occasion

1. Plates 60–2.

when she was being storm tossed while crossing the Minch, Fred was heard to say "I should have put another foot on the beam". I can just remember being taken out for a day sail from Rhu and being allowed to steer. When Fred died in 1934 *Medea* was sold. During the War she became a barrage balloon ship on the Thames and later an accommodation ship for the Norwegian Navy at Peterhead. After the War she had various owners and was eventually presented to the San Diego Maritime Museum. They did a wonderful restoration job bringing her back to her original condition. She is there today, devotedly maintained, still sailing and can be seen clearly on Google Earth alongside the larger *Star of India*.

Forceful was the first of two tugs built in 1925 for the Australian United Steamship Navigation Company and became the last coal burning steamer in Queensland. Now in the Queensland Museum, she is on show (see plate 24) and takes trips up the Brisbane River.

Albyn[2], an auxiliary ketch yacht of 46 tons, was built for the Glasgow tobacco magnate Robert French in 1934. The order was taken on at the end of the slump to keep skilled carpenters employed and she was built to a very high standard. In 1940 she was one of the many small ships to serve at Dunkirk. Refitted in 1994, she returned to the Clyde in 2009 to take part in a regatta of Mylne designed boats and still looked as good as new. Renamed *Eileen II* she was advertised for sale in 2012 at £1,390,000.

Thendara, the 87 ton auxiliary ketch, still sails the Mediterranean. After Sir ArthurYoung, the original owner, died on board of a heart attack aged 61 in 1950, she was sold and left the Clyde. In 1992 she underwent a major refit costing £1,600,000 and was advertised for sale in 2012 for just under £4,000,000. Other yachts we built in the 1930s have also survived.

2. Plate 63.

HMS Vesper, a 'V and W Class' destroyer built in 1917, served in both World Wars. For most of World War II she was on convoy duty in the Atlantic, but led the fleet into Omaha Beach on D-Day in 1943 and never received a scratch. She had been a particularly happy ship and after she was scrapped in 1945, her crew formed the HMS Vesper Association. For many years the veterans met and were royally received at Skipton, the Yorkshire town which had adopted her during the war. As grandson of the builder, I was roped in as Patron and was honoured to join the reunions. *Vesper's* battle ensign, which she flew proudly on D-Day, was spirited away by one of the crew when she was decommissioned, but having been returned anonymously, it hangs in Skipton Parish Church with its holes now skillfully repaired. By 2012 only four veterans were able to attend but a strong representation of widows, sons and daughters made up the numbers. The following year the Association was wound up leaving many happy memories.

HMS Amethyst, famous for the Yangtse Incident, still has an active and numerous Association[3], members of which took a prominent part in the 2014 Remembrance Day march past at the Cenotaph. However, the ship's fame is in danger of being overtaken by that of Simon, the ship's cat who was awarded the Dickin Medal which is often described as the animals' VC. The medal was auctioned in 1993 and fetched £23,467 and even now the mail order company Nauticalia offers cuddly 'Simon' cushions for yachtsmen.

Some ships refuse to die. After being used for Scott's Antarctic Expedition, the wooden hulled sealer *Terra Nova* built in Dundee in 1884 returned to sealing and whaling. In 1943 she suffered serious ice damage off the south-west tip of Greenland and had to be sunk to avoid becoming a hazard to

3. I am still in touch with Stewart Hett, the President of the Association. Having been my contemporary at school, he served as a lieutenant on *Amethyst* during the Yangtse Incident.

shipping. In 2012 her wreck was located on the seabed, but no serious proposition has yet been made to raise and resurrect her.

At Linthouse John Brown Engineering continued to produce gas turbines in the former Stephen Engine Works for a number of years but on their demise the property was sold again. To general surprise, the 1870 Heavy Machine Shop was classified as an 'Historic Building' and the Scottish Maritime Museum at Irvine in Ayrshire raised £30,000, including donations from the Stephen family, to take the cast iron columns and the timber roof trusses to Irvine. The graceful columns were repainted, the roof trusses repaired and the building re-erected with new brickwork, to look better than it ever had done at Linthouse. It serves as a magnificent centre for the Museum[4] although it has not so far acquired a slow speed diesel engine to display among the maritime exhibits. Almost all buildings on the Linthouse site have been demolished, but the Main Office was taken over by the Local Authority in 1990 and renamed Alexander Stephen House to provide space for start up companies. Linthouse Buildings, the tenements built in 1870 and refurbished by Jim's Linthouse Housing Association, still provides excellent homes while flats have been built on the site of the Aircraft Store. Barr and Stroud, the optical instrument makers, now Thales Optronics, took over the west end of the yard but sadly the rest remains derelict.

Plans of all ships built at Kelvinhaugh and Linthouse up to 1923 are kept by the National Maritime Museum at Greenwich and the later ones by Glasgow University. In 2012, I emptied my attic of all my Company and family papers and books, so twenty-three full cardboard boxes were handed over to the University of Glasgow Archives Department. I miss having them at home but am happy that the Stephen records are in good hands.

4. Plate 70.

Published in 2006 the book 'Shared Lives' by Maureen Borland relates how in Victorian times the Stephen family intermarried with the Templetons, the carpet manufacturers, when Young Alexander Stephen and James Templeton had married each other's sisters.

Most shipyards disappear after going bankrupt once, but Fairfield's still survives although the shipyard has collapsed five times. It went bust in 1930 and in 1963, was saved by the formation of UCS in 1968, went bust again in 1971 and, as Govan Shipbuilders was saved by nationalisation. It could have closed yet again but was taken over by Kvaerner and then BAE for warship building. At the time of writing it is threatened once more as the Royal Navy continues to shrink, but its luck may continue.

I was first interviewed for television after Stephen's had received the order for the Russian dredgers and continued to give occasional comments for BBC and ITV on events in the Industry. I appeared in 'All Their Working Lives' in 1990 which contained an hour long programme on each of Britain's main industries. The series 'Scotland's Story' followed a few years later where I spoke about the shipbuilding industry. In BBC4's 'The Men Who Built the Liners' in 2009, I was asked to give my views on why the British Shipbuilding Industry went to the dogs. I effectively represented management while the labour side was championed by Jimmy Reid who had become famous in the UCS Work-In. As that event happened after I was involved in shipbuilding, I was never able to meet him. To my surprise this programme continues to be repeated.

Jim Stephen died in 1993 and is remembered for his quiet kindliness and his first class brain. To be Chairman of his family firm during the painful decline of the Shipbuilding Industry was a cruel stroke of fate, but he faced the challenge courageously and filled his important and stressful position with honour and dignity. Ill health dogged his later years. Jim was immensely loyal to the Govan community, serving as Chairman of Linthouse Housing Association and forming Govan Housing Association, for which he was justly awarded the MBE. For many years he was an elder of Wellington Church in Glasgow and a regular follower of Scottish Opera, having been an accomplished musician on the French horn. Sadly Jim died suddenly when his son Murray, daughter Irene and six much loved grandchildren were planning a joyful celebration of his 70th birthday. He would have been immensely proud that 'Jim Stephen House' was opened by Irene for Govan Housing Association to be a superior style of sheltered housing where the inmates have their own flats – a much valued development for the community where shipyards once thrived.

I inherited Jim's papers which revealed his plans to trace all the descendants of Old Alexander Stephen's eighteen children. I took it over, contacting known cousins by telephone and letter, while searching out an increasing list of family members. Gradually the whole network evolved with considerable detective work being required as my relations had spread all over the globe. The Family Tree was published privately in 1995 on the two hundredth anniversary of Alexander's birth and records over 700 of his descendants, of whom 500 were alive at the time of publication.

In the Glasgow Necropolis Stephen family names are still inscribed on the family tomb which is a monstrous Victorian edifice of which I have become rather fond. A more restrained tombstone in a seafarers' churchyard at Footdee in Aberdeen commemorates William Stephen and other members of his family. Regrettably this monument has a list to starboard which masons dare not correct as nobody knows who or what may be lying beneath.

The Stephen family can still pull together. Thirty yards from the former Linthouse property is a vibrant organization, the Preshal Trust, where disadvantaged people are helped back onto their feet. It is run by May Nicholson, an inspiringly enlightened lady whose own recovery from addiction began in

St Kenneth's Kirk at Linthouse. The Trust Centre, which included an old container for May's office, became too small so a new building was urgently needed. £200,000 had to be raised so I sent begging letters to my family and other descendants with connections at Linthouse and they responded generously to make up a substantial percentage of the total. The Centre is up and running and now saving many people from a downward spiral, while continuing to be a wonderfully happy place.

Stephen of Linthouse 1750–1950 mentions a family tradition that a Stephen of Kineddar, where the family farmed before they became shipbuilders, was the mother of Field Marshal Prince Barclay de Tolly who commanded the Russian army at the time of Napoleon's invasion in 1811. Research showed this not so but she was probably his great-great-grandmother. Barclays had emigrated from Towie, later corrupted to Tolly, in Aberdeenshire, to Riga in Estonia where as merchants they traded with Scotland. It is probable that a young Barclay on business in the port of Lossiemouth met and married a Miss Stephen whose home was less than a mile away. The Field Marshall's great-grandfather was Johan Stephan Barclay, probably named in the Scottish tradition after his maternal grandfather John. This link is not proven but another link confirms that I can confidently claim Barclay de Tolly as a relation.

In 2005 Sue and I visited the 1812 Gallery in the Hermitage at St Petersburg where portraits of the 332 Russian generals who fought against Napoleon are hung. All the names were in Russian so we asked our guide if she could point out Barclay de Tolly and she immediately indicated one of only four full length portraits. When we mentioned that he was a relation our stock rose considerably. The portrait was too high up to get a good photograph so we tried to buy one, only to be met with the typical Russian 'Niet'. Our hotel manager, who had dealings with the Hermitage, also tried and failed. Later Sue mentioned this to her cousin Dr Nigel Allan, now retired from the Wellcome Trust, whose colleague Nicholaj Serikoff had contacts at the Hermitage but even he had difficulty. As no stepladder was available, he sat on another man's shoulders holding the camera above his head to take the photograph shown in plate 52. When we met Nicholaj later, he insisted that I had the same facial bone structure as Barclay de Tolly.

Mention must be made about the bad publicity Alexander Stephen & Sons still receives on account of *Daphne* which capsized immediately after her launch in 1883 drowning 127 men. The Company was certainly at fault, but this horrific accident now tends to be judged by today's standards. In those days no launch stability calculations were available to any shipbuilder as launching was by rule of thumb. In this case the Shipowners were desperate to take possession of their ship in time for the Glasgow Fair and the Company was doing its best to satisfy an important customer. This resulted in machinery, material and workmen being moved onto the ship before the launch and, due to the haste, some of the side doors were not properly closed. The Government Commission of Enquiry exonerated the Company but thereafter no launch took place in any yard until stability calculations had been made. Today's critics claim that the Enquiry was a whitewash, but it was not by the standards which existed in Victorian times when serious accidents in Industry were all too common. Claims have also been made that widows and children were left to starve and received no compensation. In fact, the substantial Public Relief Fund raised far more to compensate the dependants than was normal at that time. It was a sad and sorry event in the history of Alexander Stephen & Sons but it is wrong that we should be remembered for one launch which went wrong rather than 1,000 which were successful.

My Stephen ancestors regretted this disaster immeasurably and my family shares their sadness to this day so I would like this book to end on a happier note with an extract from the Linthouse News.

THE ARK – SHIP NO 1
(with apologies to Genesis)

The Lord said unto Noahrie[5] "Where is the Ark I commanded thee to build?" and Noahrie said unto the Lord "Verily, verily mine gopher wood merchant hath let me down – yea even though it hath been on order for 12 months and, my beloved son WatShem[6] hath drawn plans for the Ark with a breadth of 30 cubits and a height of 50 cubits while thy specification clearly sayeth breadth 50 cubits and height 30 cubits. What can I do O Lord?" God said unto Noahrie "I want that Ark finished even after forty days and forty nights" and Noahrie said "It will be so". But it was not.

Then sayeth the Lord "What seemeth to be the trouble this time?" Noahrie rent his garments and said "The gopher wood is definitely in transit but the tablets of stone with delivery instructions thereon gotteth broken asunder and even my other beloved son JackShem[7] spendeth his time writing poems for the Linthouse News. Lord, I am undone". And lo, it was not fulfilled.

And Noahrie said unto the Lord "Mine pitch daubers, the black squad, hath an overtime ban and disputeth the demarcation with mine gopher wood carpenters as to who painteth the window and the door". But the wrath of the Lord was kindled and he said "What about the beasts of the field and the fowls of the air which I commanded thee to keep alive? Where are the giraffes?" And Noahrie answered "They cometh by van on Thursday". And the Lord said "What about the clean beasts and the rats?" Noahrie answered "Verily some bastard hath nicked Joe the Ratcatcher's[8] traps, but lo, here

5. Norrie McCrae was Shipyard Director.
6. David Watson was Naval Architect.
7. Jackson Robertson was Planning Manager and Linthouse News poet laureate writing doggerel verse.
8. Joe was full time ratcatcher, well known to everybody.

cometh the Beavers[9] two by two from the Paint Store and the Fox[10] from the Smithy and yonder are a few Birdwisas[11] of the air".

But the Lord said "Where are the unicorns?" and Noahrie wrung his hands and wept exceeding bitter saying "Lord, they are a discontinued line – thou canst not get unicorns for love nor money". The Lord said "Where are the other beasts of the field – the Wolf, the Mastiff and the Ribbock or the fowls of the air – the Eagle, the Woodlark, the Mallard and Puffin even unto the British Fulmar and the British Curlew[12]?" And Noahrie answered "The beasts of the field hath been delivered into the hands of Harland and Wolff and Cammel Laird and the fowls of the air to Swan Hunter[13]; and as for mine Engineers, they said that seven days and seven nights would get the engine working, but even now they complain about the tensile strength of the cedars of Lebanon and keep muttering something about a burning bush". The Lord said "But Noahrie, engines hath not been specified as they hath not yet been invented".

Noahrie put on sackcloth and ashes and prostrated himself upon the earth, weeping and gnashing his teeth exceeding sore and said "Lord, Lord thou knowest what it is like with delivery dates". And the Lord in his infinite wisdom and loving kindness looked down and said "Noahrie my son I know. Why else dost thou think I have caused a flood to descend upon the Earth?"

9. Dick Beavers was Head Foreman Painter.
10. Jimmy Fox was Head Foreman Blacksmith.
11. Jimmy Birdwisa was Head Foreman Carpenter and later Fitting Out Manager.
12. All names of Stephen built ships.
13. Three rival shipbuilders.

APPENDIX

List of Ships Built by Alexander Stephen & Sons

Ships built by Alexander Stephen & Sons at Aberdeen

Note. Although no records of ships built at Aberdeen before 1813 are available, it is safe to assume that vessels constructed before that date were chiefly brigs, sloops and schooners ordered by local owners for fishing or trading. Ships were not allocated Yard Numbers as later.

Type of Ship	*Name of Ship*	*Dimensions*	*Builders' Old Tonnage*	*Built for*	*Owners' Port*	*Completed*
Brig or snow	*Glory*	89'10" × 25'10" × 16'6"	248	John Catto and others	Aberdeen	Dec. 1813
Brig or snow	*Blucher*	68'11" × 21'0" × 11'3"	125	Alex Thom and others	Aberdeen	June 1814
Brigantine	*Adelphi*	68'0" × 20'9" × 11'7"	122	Wm Stephen jnr and others*	Aberdeen	Sep. 1814
Schooner	*Olive*	61'1" × 18'7" × 9'10"	89	John Fleming and others*	Aberdeen	March 1817
Brig or snow	*Duncan Forbes*	67'11" × 21'9" × 12'4"	134	Alex Forbes and others	Aberdeen	April 1817
Brigantine	*Star*	78'11" × 22'11" x14'3"	172	Alex Gibbon and others*	Aberdeen	March 1818
Brigantine	*Ann*	78'8" × 24'3" × 15'0"	196	John Fleming and others*	Aberdeen	Aug. 1818
Brigantine	*Latona*	84'6" × 24'10" x15'9"	221	Alex Gibbon and others*	Aberdeen	Feb. 1819
Brig or snow	*Arethusa*	87'4" × 25'0" × 15'11"	236	Wm Stephen jnr and others	Aberdeen	April 1820
Schooner	?	56'7" × 18'6" × 10'1"	82	?	?	Jan. 1821
Schooner	*Enterprize*	57'5½' × 18'7" × 10'7½"	83	R Spring and others	Aberdeen	March 1823
Brigantine	*Unicorn*	75'9" × 22'5½" × 14'5"	165	Wm Stephen and J. Fleming	Aberdeen	July 1823
Brigantine	*Atlantic*	84'6" × 24'2½" × 16'0"	217	R Catto and others	Aberdeen	Feb. 1824
Brigantine	*Sir R Barclay*	65'6" × 20'0" × 11'1"	111	A Mortimer and others	Aberdeen	Sep. 1824
Brigantine	*Earl of Fife*	66'4"x 20'0½" × 11'6"	113	A Mortimer and others	Aberdeen	May 1825
Brigantine	*Bolivar*	85'9" × 24'6" × 16'6"	224	J Fleming and others	Aberdeen	June 1825
Brigantine	*James Hadden*	75'3" × 21'10½" × 14'0"	156	A. Mortimer and others	Aberdeen	Feb. 1826
Brigantine	*Matchless*	79'9" × 23'2½" × 15'5"	188	Wm Simpson and others	Aberdeen	July 1826
Schooner	*Aid*	67'2" × 20'4" × 12'7"	121	Mr Chapel	Arbroath	1826

* indicates a minor share in ownership by a member of the Stephen family

Ships built by Alexander Stephen & Sons at Aberdeen – continued

Type of Ship	*Name of Ship*	*Dimensions*	*Builders' Old Tonnage*	*Built for*	*Owners' Port*	*Completed*
Sloop	*Young George*	50'1" × 17'5" × 9'4"	64	Captain Ritchie	Rosehearty	1827
Schooner	*Henry M'chie*	57'8" × 18'3" × 10'6½"	83	R. Leith and others*	Aberdeen	March 1827
Brigantine	*Rosalinde*	68'3" × 20'9" × 12'6"	129	Mr Clarkson	Aberdeen	1828
Smack	*Sarah*	43'9" × 14'10½" × 8'1½"	41	James Dick	Aberdeen	May 1828
Brigantine	*Abbotsford*	65'4" × 20'9" × 12'5"	121	R. Spring and others	Aberdeen	Aug. 1829

* indicates a minor share in ownership by a member of the Stephen family

Ships built by Alexander Stephen & Sons at Arbroath

Yard No.	Type of Ship	Name of Ship	Dimensions	Builders' old Tonnage	Built for	Owners' Port	Completed
	Sloop	*Ann*	46'8" × 17'0" × 9'0"	56	James Cay	—	1830
1	Schooner	*Helen*	71'4" × 20'11½" × 12'9"	137	John Peatt & Son	—	1830
2	Schooner	*Margaret*	68'7" × 19'9½" × 12'9"	118	Mr Renny	—	1831
3	Schooner	*Euphemia*	71'1" × 20'8½"× 12'9"	134	Mr Mills	Arbroath	1831
4	—	*Royal William*	70'4" × 19'8" × 12'0"	120	Mr Livies	—	1831
5	—	*Broathwick*	75'10" × 21'0" × 13'2"	148	Mr Chapel	Arbroath	1832
6	Schooner	*Hope*	75'6" × 21'1½" × 13'3'"	149	Mr D. Muir	Montrose	1932
7	Schooner	*Majestic*	78'3" × 21'1¾" × 13'9"	156	Mr Mills	Arbroath	1832
8	Brigantine	*Oporto*	73'10" × 19'10½" × 12'5½"	130	Mr John Mitchell	Glasgow	1833
9	—	*Ann* (II)	67'2¼" × 19'2" × 11'8"	109	John Cargill	Arbroath	1833
10	Sloop	*Reaper*	50'10'" × 16'6" × 8'6"	59	Capt. D. Peter	Montrose	1833
11	Brig	*Themis*	67'4" × 20'3¼" × 12'5½"	121	Mr Chapel	Arbroath	1834
12	Schooner	*Juno*	72'3'" × 21'6" × 13'1"	146	David Paterson	—	1834
13	Schooner	*Mentor*	72'7" × 21'3½" × 13'5"	144	Andson, Allan & Chapel	Arbroath	1835
14	Snow	*Romulus*	78'11" × 21'7" × 13'3"	164	Capt. D. L. Cargill	Arbroath	1836
15	—	*Lady Jane*	70'0" × 21'0" × 12'8"	138	Capt. W. Logan	Arbroath	1836
16	Snow	*David Grant*	83'11" × 22'10" × 14'0'"	195	Mr Lawrence	Arbroath	1837
17	Schooner	*Hamille Mitchell*	75'6" × 22'2" × 13'10"	166	Mr John Mitchell	Glasgow	1837
18	Barque	*Anne*	88'0" × 22'10½" × 14'6"	207	Charles Kidd & Co.	Arbroath	1838
19	Brig	*Mary's Brig*	82'2" × 22'9" × 13'8½"	189	Capt. Thos Leslie	Aberdeen	1838
20	Brig	*Ariel*	82'11" × 22'8" × 14'3"	189	T. Couper & Sons	Dundee	1839
21	Schooner	*John Mitchell*	121'2" × 26'7½" × 18'6"	402	Mr John Mitchell	Glasgow	1839
22	Brig	*Jessie Greig*	91'0" × 22'10'" × 14'10"	220	Andrew Greig	Dundee	1840

Ships built by Alexander Stephen & Sons at Arbroath – continued

Yard No.	Type of Ship	Name of Ship	Dimensions	Builders' old Tonnage	Built for	Owners' Port	Completed
23	Snow	*Adino*	92'0" × 22'11" ×15'0"	219	Leslie & Co.	Dundee	1840
24	Barque	*Royal Archer*	101'4" × 24'7" × 16'10"	278	W. & I. Fleming	Glasgow	1841
25	Barque	*Peruvian*	102'8" × 24'7½" × 16'10"	283	Alex. Pitcaithly	Newburgh	1841
26	Brig	*Eden Bank*	83'4'" × 22'11" × 14'9"	194	T. Couper & Sons	Dundee	1841
27	Barque	*Britannia*	105'9"x 25'3" × 18'0"	308	Alex. Stephen & Sons	Arbroath	1842
28	Schooner	*Isabella*	64'0" × 19'0" × 10'6"	102	Allen & Co.	Arbroath	1841
29	Brig	*Prince Albert*	94'6" × 23'10" × 16'0"	256	D. Peat	Arbroath	1842
30	Brig	*Jessie*	64'3" × 17'7" × 9'6"	88	Mr Just	Dundee	1842
31	Brig	*Laurel*	63'10" × 17'6'" × 9'6"	87	T. Couper & Sons	Dundee	1842
32	Brig	*Eliza*	86'3" × 22'3" × 14'4"	191	Mr Jack	Dundee	1843

Ships built by Alexander Stephen & Sons at Dundee

Yard No.	Type of Ship	Name of Ship	Dimensions	Builders' old Tonnage (gross*)	Built for	Owners' Port	Completed
1	Brig	*Diana*	86'2" × 22'3" × 14'3"	191	A. Blives	Dundee	1844
2	Schooner	*Jules*	70'3" × 19'9" × 11'7"	123	Baxter Bros.	Dundee	1844
3	Barque	*Brechin Castle*	115'3" × 25'8" × 17'5"	371	Baxter Bros.	Dundee	1844
4	Barque	*Richard Cobden*	116'6" × 25'11" × 17'8"	361	Wm Small	Dundee	1845
5	Snow	*Cathereen*	86'6" × 22'2" × 14'6"	192	Mr Fenwick	Dundee	1845
6	Barque	*Queen*	115'3" × 25'8" × 17'5"	370	D. Martin & Co.	Dundee	1846
7	Snow	*William*	87'2" × 22'5" × 14'7"	197	Scott & Murdo	Dundee	1846
8	Brig	*Neva*	88'8" × 23'5" × 14'5"	218	Andrew Low	Dundee	1847
9	Snow	*Netta*	85'8" × 21'0" × 12'6"	172	D. Martin & Co.	Dundee	1847
10	Barque	*Jean Andson*	106'5" × 23'6" × 15'6"	274	Andson & Duncan	Arbroath	1847
11	Barque	*Asia*	139'0" × 25'5" × 19'8"	548	Alex. Stephen & Sons	Dundee	1848
12	Barque	*Europe* (Troop Ship *Dudbrook*)	143'6" × 28'6" × 20'4"	551	Mr Mann	London	1848
13	Brig	*Duna*	93'2" × 23'3" × 14'6"	228	A. Low, Junr	Dundee	1849
14	Ship	*Amazon*	144'0" × 31'6" × 21'6"	791	J. & F. Somes	London	1850
15	Ship	*Cossipore*	148'7" × 28'8" × 21'0"	838	W. S. Lindsay	London	1851
16	Brig	*Elizabeth Duncan*	94'5" × 23'2" × 14'5"	228	Mr Westland	Aberdeen	1851
17	Ship, Wood	*Harkaway*	167'8" × 32'4" × 21'0"	830	J. & F. Somes	London	1852
18	Ship, Wood	*Polmaise*	178'9" × 32'2" × 21'2"	878	Mr Campbell	Glasgow	1853
19	Ship, Wood	*Whirlwind*	187'0" × 33'6" × 21'1"	1003	J. & F. Somes	London	1854
20	Ship, Wood	*Bumah*	188'0" × 33'6" × 21'2"	1020	A. Willis and Co.	Liverpool	1855
21	Ship, Wood	*Eastern Monarch*	239'0" × 40'3" × 24'9"	1849	J. & F. Somes	London	1856

Ships built by Alexander Stephen & Sons at Dundee – continued

Yard No.	*Type of Ship*	*Name of Ship*	*Dimensions*	*Builders' old Tonnage (gross*)*	*Built for*	*Owners' Port*	*Completed*
22	Barque (Wood)	*Dartmouth*	185'4" × 34'3" × 21'6"	*978	J. & F. Somes	London	1859
23	Barque (Wood)	Ianthe	135'6" × 26'0" × 16'6"	380	L. Tulloch & Co.	Sunderland	1858
24	Sealer & Whaler	*Narwhal*	151'4" × 30'1" × 18'5"	*533	Dundee S. & W. Fishing Co.	Dundee	1859
25	Barque (Wood)	*Star of India*	190'4" × 34'2" × 22'1"	*1092	J. & F. Somes	London	1861
26	Sealer & Whaler	*Camperdown*	154'5" × 30'0" × 18'6"	*541	Dundee S. & W. Fishing Co.	Dundee	1860
27	Sealer & Whaler	*Polynia*	146'2" × 29'0" × 18'1"	*472	Dundee S. & W. Fishing Co.	Dundee	1861
28	Barque (Wood)	*Earl Dalhousie* (I)	191'5" × 34'8" × 22'2"	1047	Alex. Stephen & Sons	Dundee	1862
29	Barque (Wood)	*The Sir Jamsetjee Family*	192'8" × 34'8" × 21'9"	1049	Cursetjee Jamsetjee (*Per* Forbes & Co.)	Bombay	1863
30	Sealer & Whaler	*Wolf* (I)	131'5" × 25'4" × 13'3"	400	Walter Grieve	Greenock	1863
31	Sealer & Whaler	*Alexander*	149'0" × 29'2" × 18'6"	590	Gilroy Bros	Dundee	1864
32	Sealer & Whaler	*Erik*	157'8" × 29'5" × 18'5"	*533	G. Gibbs	London	1865
33	Sealer & Whaler	*Esquimaux*	157'3" × 29'5" × 19'3"	*593	Dundee S. & W. Fishing Co.	Dundee	1865
34	Sealer & Whaler	*Retriever*	138'0" × 26'5" × 15'5"	462	Ridley, Son & Co.	Liverpool	1865
35	Barque (Composite)	*Corona*	209'6" × 35'0" × 22'0"	*1202	Alex. Stephen & Sons	Dundee	1866
36	Sealer & Whaler	*Nimrod*	136'0" × 26'9" × 16'0"	*334	Job Bros	Liverpool	1866
37	Ship (Composite)	*Sree Singapura*	164'8" × 27'7" × 17'5"	585	McTaggart & Co.	London	1866
38	Sealer & Whaler	*Mastiff*	137'4" × 26'9" × 16'1"	*360	JohnMunn	Harbour Grace Newfoundland	1867
39	Sealer & Whaler	*Arctic* (I)	158'0" × 29'3" × 19'5"	*567	Alex. Stephen & Sons	Dundee	1867
40	—	*Unnamed*	Destroyed in Fire	—	—	—	—

Note. All Sealing and Whaling Vessels are Wood and Auxiliary Steam.

Ships built by Alexander Stephen & Sons at Dundee – continued

Yard No.	*Type of Ship*	*Name of Ship*	*Dimensions*	*Builders' old Tonnage (gross*)*	*Built for*	*Owners' Port*	*Completed*
Yard totally destroyed by fire							1868
41	Barque (Composite)	*Tonbridge*	181'0" × 32'0" × 19'4"	856	J. H. Luscombe	London	1869
42	Barque (Composite)	*Laju*	162'0" × 28'0" × 17'6"	556	Dundee Shipowning Co. (W. O. Taylor, Manager)	Dundee	1869
43	Steamer (Iron)	*Cheops*	255'0" × 33'2" × 24'5"	*1505	Alex. Stephen & Sons (Sold to Shaw Maxton and Co., 1885)	Dundee	1870
44	Barque (Composite)	*Woodlark*	182'4" × 32'1" × 19'3"	*890	Alex. Stephen & Sons	Dundee	1870
45	Sealer & Whaler	*Commodore*	151'0" × 27'1" × 16'5"	*427	John Munn	Harbour Grace Newfoundland	1871
46	Sealer	*Hector*	151'1" × 27'1" × 16'6"	*473	Job Bros.	Liverpool	1870
47	Sealer & Whaler	*Eagle*	156'4" × 28'7" × 18'1"	*506	N. F. Sealing & Wh. Co. (C. T. Bowring Bros)	St Johns Newfoundland	1871
48	Steamer (Iron)	*Cyphrenes*	300'0" × 34'1" × 25'5"	*1994	Alex. Stephen & Sons	Dundee	1872
49	Steamer (Iron)	*American*	320'0" × 34'2" × 19'7"	*2126	Union S.S. Co.	Southampton	1873
50	Sealer & Whaler	*Ranger*	161'1" × 28'7" × 18'0"	*520	Robert Alexander	St Johns, N. F.	1871
51	Sealer & Whaler	*Wolf* (II)	165'9" × 28'8" × 18'0"	*520	Walter Grieve	Greenock	1871
52	Sealer & Whaler	*Iceland*	150'5" × 27'3" × 16'4"	*423	D. Murray & Son	Glasgow	1872
53	Sealer	*Discovery* (*Bloodhound*)	160'0" × 32'2" × 18'3"	396	British War Vessel	London	1873
54	Sealer	*Proteus*	190'4" × 29'9" × 18'6"	*687	J. W. Stewart	Greenock	1873
55	Sealer	*Neptune*	190'5" × 29'8" × 18'4"	*684	Job Bros	Liverpool	1872

Note. All Sealing and Whaling Vessels are Wood and Auxiliary Steam.

Ships built by Alexander Stephen & Sons at Dundee – continued

Yard No.	*Type of Ship*	*Name of Ship*	*Dimensions*	*Builders' old Tonnage (gross*)*	*Built for*	*Owners' Port*	*Completed*
56	Sealer	*Bear*	190'4" × 29'9" × 18'6"	*689	W. Grieve	Greenock	1874
57	Sailing Ship (Iron)	*Lochee*	264'2" × 39'0" × 23'4"	*1812	Dundee Clipper Line	Dundee	1875
58	Sealer	*Arctic* (II)	200'6" × 31'6" × 19'9"	*828	Alex. Stephen & Sons	Dundee	1875
59	Barque (Iron)	*Edith Lorn*	200'1" × 32'3" × 10'9"	*847	Dundee Shipowning Co. (W. O. Taylor, *Manager*)	Dundee	1876
60	Sailing Ship (Iron)	*Duntrune*	245'2" × 38'3" × 23'0"	*1565	Dundee Clipper Line	Dundee	1875
61	Sailing Ship (Iron)	*Maulesden*	245'2" × 38'3" × 23'1"	*1554	Dundee Clipper Line	Dundee	1875
62	Sealer	*Aurora*	165'2" × 30'6" × 18'9"	*580	Alex. Stephen & Sons	Dundee	1876
63	Barque (Iron)	*Aithernie Castle*	233'5" × 36'2" × 21'3"	*1260	Geo. Duncan	Liverpool	1876
64	Sailing Ship (Iron)	*Glamis*	225'3" × 34'8" × 21'9"	*1205	Dundee Clipper Line	Dundee	1876
65	Sailing Ship (Iron)	*Southesk*	225'2" × 35'0" × 21'8"	*1210	Dundee Clipper Line	Dundee	1877
66	Barque (Iron)	*Glengarry*	199'8" × 32'2" × 19'1"	*844	Dundee Shipowning Co. (W. O. Taylor, *Manager*)	Dundee	1877
67	Barque (Iron)	*Stuart*	202'5" × 34'2" × 19'1"	*912	J. Hay & Co.	Liverpool	1877
68	Barque (Iron)	*Overdale*	203'3" × 34'2" × 19'2"	*912	J. Hay & Co.	Liverpool	1877
69	Barque (Iron)	*Edgbaston*	203'2" × 34'2" × 19'2"	*912	T. Frost, Junr	Liverpool	1878
70	Barque (Iron)	*Easterhill*	202'5" × 32'1" × 18'8"	*915	R. Gilchrist & Co.	Glasgow	1878
71	Barque (Iron)	*Helenslea* (I)	228'0" × 35'2" × 21'8"	*1248	Alex. Stephen & Sons	Dundee	1879
72	Barque (Iron)	*Victorine*	233'5" × 36'2" × 21'3"	*1253	Ant. Dom. Bordes	Paris	1879
73	Sealer & Whaler	*Resolute*	175'5" × 30'7" × 18'6"	*624	Dundee S. & W. Fishing Co.	Dundee	1880
74	Sealer & Whaler	*Thetis* (I)	181'1" × 30'9" × 19'1"	*723	Alex. Stephen & Sons (American War Vessel)	Dundee	1881

Note. All Sealing and Whaling Vessels are Wood and Auxiliary Steam.

Ships built by Alexander Stephen & Sons at Dundee – continued

Yard No.	*Type of Ship*	*Name of Ship*	*Dimensions*	*Builders' old Tonnage (gross*)*	*Built for*	*Owners' Port*	*Completed*
75	Steamer (Iron)	*North Sea*	230'0" x 30'9" x 15'9"	*1117	Dundee, Perth & London Shipping Co.	Dundee	1881
76	Steamer (Iron)	*White Sea*	230'3" x 30'7" x 15'9"	*1119	Dundee, Perth & London Shipping Co.	Dundee	1881
77	Barque (Iron)	*Glenfarg*	203'8" x 34'1" x 19'1"	*898	Dundee Shipowning Co. (W. O. Taylor, *Manager*)	Dundee	1881
78	Barque (Iron)	Glenshee	203'8" x 34'1" x 19'1"	*895	Dundee Shipowning Co. (W. O. Taylor, *Manager*)	Dundee	1882
79	Barque (Steel)	*Helenslea* (II)	249'8" x 35'4" x 21'6"	*1374	Alex. Stephen & Sons	Dundee	1882
80	Barque (Steel)	*Glenfyne*	213'8" x 34'2" x 19'1"	*957	Dundee Shipowning Co. (W. O. Taylor, *Manager*)	Dundee	1882
81	Barque (Steel)	*Glenogle*	213'8" x 34'2" x 19'1"	*958	Dundee Shipowning Co. (W. O. Taylor, *Manager*)	Dundee	1883
82	Barque (Steel)	*Earl of Dalhousie* (II)	264'0" x 38'7" x 23'4"	*1765	Alex. Stephen & Sons	Dundee	1884
83	Steamer (Steel)	*Thane*	245'0" x 33'2" x 20'6"	*1351	R. A. Mudie & Son	Dundee	1883
84	Sealer	*Terra Nova*	187'0" x 31'0" x 19'0"	*744	Alex. Stephen & Sons	Dundee	1884
85	Barque (Steel)	*Thetis* (II)	248'5" x 35'4" x 21'6"	*1352	Alex. Stephen & Sons	Dundee	1885
86	Barque (Steel and Iron)	*Doris*	248'6" x 35'3" x 21'6"	*1353	Alex. Stephen & Sons	Dundee	1887
87	Barque (Steel)	*Eudora*	287'5" x 40'5" x 23'7"	*1992	Alex. Stephen & Sons	Dundee	1888
88	—	North Carr Lightship	—	—	Northern Lights Commissioners	Edinburgh	1889
89	Barque (Steel and Iron)	*Newfield* (I)	248'6" x 35'3" x 21'6"	1306	Brownelles & Co.	Liverpool	1889

Note. All Sealing and Whaling Vessels are Wood and Auxiliary Steam.

Ships built by Alexander Stephen & Sons at Dundee – continued

Yard No.	Type of Ship	Name of Ship	Dimensions	Builders' old Tonnage (gross*)	Built for	Owners' Port	Completed
90	Barque (Wood)	*Diana*	151'1" × 24'1" × 16'6"	*473	Job Bros.	Liverpool	1891
91	Barque (Steel and Iron)	*Galena*	292'0" × 42'0" × 24'0"	*2294	Alex. Stephen & Sons	Dundee	1890
92	Barque (Steel and Iron)	*Mayhill*	292'0" × 41'0" × 23'7"	*2121	W. & J. Myres Sons & Co.	Liverpool	1890
93	Barque (Steel and Iron)	*Annie Speer*	243'0" × 37'1" × 21'6"	*1540	Brownelles & Co.	Liverpool	1891
94	Barque (Steel and Iron)	*Kirkhill*	243'0" × 37'1" × 21'6"	*1540	John Steel & Son	Liverpool	1891
95	Barque (Steel and Iron)	*Melita*	310'0" × 45'2" × 25'2"	*2946	Alex. Stephen & Sons	Dundee	1892
96	Barque (Steel)	*Pitlochry*	319'5" × 45'2" × 26'5"	*3088	Alex. Stephen & Sons (Afterwards sold to Laisz, Hamburg)	Dundee	1894
97	Barque (Steel)	*Newfield* (II)	249'2" × 37'2" × 21'5"	*1512	Brownelles & Co.	Dundee	1893

Ships built by Alexander Stephen & Sons at Kelvinhaugh

Yard No.	*Type of Ship*	*Name of Ship*	*Dimensions*	*Builders' old Tonnage (gross*)*	*Built for*	*Owners' Port*	*Completed*
1	Wood Sailer	*Cyclone*	151'8" × 26'4" × 19'2"	594	Catto & Son	Aberdeen	1853
2	Iron Sailer	*Typhoon*	190'0" × 32'6" × 22'6"	780	Cannon & Sons	Liverpool	1852
3	Iron Sailer	*Hurricane*	214'9" × 30'7" × 20'0"	980	Martin & Co.	Gt. St. Helens, London	1853
4	Iron P.S.	*Myrtle*	172'0" × 23'6" × 14'0"	590	*Unknown*	—	1853
5	Iron P.S.	*Wm McCormick*	205'0" × 28'0" × 16'6"	840	Derry Company	Derry	1854
6	Iron Sailer	*John Bell*	220'0" × 33'0" × 22'0"	*997	Bell Brothers	Glasgow	1854
7	Iron Sailer	*Storm Cloud*	195'3" × 30'0" × 20'4"	789	Alex. Stephen & Sons	Glasgow	1854
8	Iron Sailer	*White Eagle*	195'4" × 32'9" × 22'3"	1072	Alex. Stephen & Sons	Glasgow	1855
9	Iron S.S.	*Euphrates*	228'0" × 35'0" × 22'0"	1348	Alex. Stephen & Sons	Glasgow	1855
10	Iron S.S.	*Semaphore*	200'0" × 24'0" × 16'6"	715	*Unknown*	Glasgow	1855
11	Iron P.S.	*Blazer*	150'0" × 23'0' × 13'0"	383	Liverpool Tug Co.	Liverpool	1856
12	Wood Sailer	*Tyburnia*	185'0" × 34'0" × 22'0"	1012	J. & F. Somes	London	1857
13	Iron S.S.	*Bee*	96'0" × 16'0" × 9'0"	118	*Unknown*	—	1856
14	Iron Sailer	*Charlemagne*	195'0" × 33'0" × 21'0"	1014	Catto & Son	Aberdeen	1857
15	Iron P.S.	*Prince Albert*	192'0" × 24'0" × 14'6"	*524	Aberdeen, Leith & Clyde S.N. Co.	Aberdeen	1857
16	Iron S.S.	*Dahomé*	165'0" × 24'6" × 15'6"	479	Regis Ainée	Marseilles	1857
17	Iron Sailer	*Sea Queen*	180'0" × 30'0" × 21'0"	775	J. H. Watt	Glasgow	1858
18	Iron Barque	*Edith Preston*	154'0" × 25'0" × 17'6"	490	E. Preston	London	1859
19	Iron Sailer	*City of Lucknow*	192'0" × 30'0" × 21'0"	859	George Smith & Sons	Glasgow	1859
20	Iron Barque	*Carnatic*	162'0" × 27'0" × 18'9"	566	G. L. Munro	London	1859
21	Iron Brigantine	*Angelita*	100'0" × 16'6" × 11'6"	134	Nelson, Ismay & Co.	Liverpool	1859

Ships built by Alexander Stephen & Sons at Kelvinhaugh – continued

Yard No.	*Type of Ship*	*Name of Ship*	*Dimensions*	*Builders' old Tonnage (gross*)*	*Built for*	*Owners' Port*	*Completed*
22	Iron Sailer	*Clyde*	200'0' × 33'0" × 22'10"	1044	J. & F. Somes	London	1860
23	Iron Sailer	*City of Madras*	200'0" × 31'8" × 21'10"	967	George Smith & Sons	Glasgow	1859
24	Iron S.S.	*Cora Linn*	140'0" × 18'6" × 11'0"	234	Handyside & Henderson (Anchor Line)	Glasgow	1859
25	Iron S.S.	*Ailsa Craig*	140'0" × 18'6" × 11'0"	234	Handyside & Henderson (Anchor Line)	Glasgow	1860
26	Iron Dredger	No. —	80'0" × 23'0" × 8'10½"	240	Clyde Trust	Glasgow	1860
27	Iron Sailer	*City of Calcutta*	200'0" × 31'8" × 21'10"	967	George Smith & Sons	Glasgow	1860
28	Iron S.S.	*Coringa*	900'0" × 27'6" × 15' 8½"	765	British India S.N. Co.	Glasgow	1861
29	Iron Schooner	*Mexico*	100'0" × 20'0" × 11'9"	187	Nelson, Ismay & Co.	Liverpool	1861
30	Iron Barque	*Ismay*	140'0" × 26'0" × 17'0"	447	Nelson, Ismay & Co.	Liverpool	1861
31	Iron Barque	*Dunnikier*	147'0" × 25'4" × 17'0"	450	Thomas Skinner	Glasgow	1861
32	Iron Sailer	*Wave Queen*	180'0" × 30'0" × 21'2½"	775	J. H. Watt	Glasgow	1861
33	Iron Sailer	*City of Bombay*	200'0" × 31'8" × 21'10"	967	George Smith & Sons	Glasgow	1862
34	W. & I. Sailer	*John Lidgett*	178'7" × 30'0" × 20'6"	770	J. Lidgett & Sons	London	1862
35	W. & I. Sailer	*Arima*	170'0" × 29'6" × 20'0"	704	G. Turnbull & Co.	—	1862
36	Iron Sailer	*City of Cashmere*	200'0" × 31'8" × 21'10"	967	George Smith & Sons	Glasgow	1863
37	Iron Brig	*Belle of the Mersey*	106'0" × 21'6" × 11'9"	229	George Eastee	Liverpool	1862
38	Iron Barque	*Black Watch*	153'0" × 26'10" × 17'8"	524	Lennox, Nephew & Co.	New Broad St London	1862
39	Iron Barque	*Glencoyn*	140'0" × 26'2" × 16'10"	452	H. W. Hewitt	Whitehaven	1863
40	W. & I. Brigantine	*Arriero*	105'0" × 21'0" × 11'9"	216	T. H. Ismay & Co.	Liverpool	1862
41	Iron Sailer	*Severn*	180'0" × 30'0" × 21'2½"	775	J. H. Watt	Glasgow	1863

Ships built by Alexander Stephen & Sons at Kelvinhaugh – continued

Yard No.	*Type of Ship*	*Name of Ship*	*Dimensions*	*Builders' old Tonnage (gross*)*	*Built for*	*Owners' Port*	*Completed*
42	W. & I. S.S.	*Sea King**	222'7" × 32'8" × 20'6"	1152	Robertson & Co.	Glasgow	1863
43	Iron Sailer	*Bothwell Castle*	170'0" × 28'0" × 18'5"	638	Thomas Skinner	Glasgow	1863
44	W. & I. Sailer	*Eliza Shaw*	180'0" × 30'6" × 18'6"	800	Killick & Martin	—	1863
45	Iron Barque	*Pembroke Castle*	140'0" × 26'2" × 16'4"	452	J. H. Simpson	Swansea	1863
46	Iron Brigantine	*Zircon*	105'0" × 21'0" × 12'6"	216	R. Tedcastle & Co.	Dublin	1863
47	Iron Sailer	*Woosung*	170'7" × 31'2" × 19'3"	784	W. B. Boodle	Birkenhead	1863
48	Iron P.S.	*Fergus*	210'0" × 23'0" × 9'6"	552	N. Mathieson	Glasgow	1863
49	Iron Sailer	*City of Lahore*	202'0" × 31'8" × 21'10"	976	George Smith & Sons	Glasgow	1864
50	W. & I. Sailer	*Hoang Ho*	170'0" × 28'6" × 17'6"	668	Smith, Preston & Co.	Liverpool	1864
51	W. & I. Sailer	*Janet Ferguson*	157'0" × 28'6" × 18'0"	604	Bain Brothers	Dumbarton	1864
52	Iron P.S.	*The Dare*	210'0" × 23'0" × 9' 6"	552	E. Miller	London	1863
53	W. & I. Sailer	*Gossamer*	180'0" × 30'6" × 18'8¼"	800	Potter Brothers	Liverpool	1864
54	W. & I. Sailer	*Mofussilite*	200'0" × 33'0" × 21'0"	1043	Finlay, Campbell & Co.	London	1864
55	Iron P.S.	*Luzon*	180'0" × 26'0" × 14'0"	591	Ker, Bolton & Co.	Glasgow	1864
56	Iron Sailer	*Lucerne*	162'0" × 28'2¼" × 18'9"	613	G. L. Munro	London	1864
57	Iron P.S.	*Lake Ontario*	180'3" × 27'2" × 10'0"	643	J. & A. Allan	Glasgow	1864
58	Iron P.S.	*Bay of Kandy*	176'0" × 26'11" × 8'6"	615	J. & A. Allan	Glasgow	1864
59	Iron Sailer	*Copernicus*	155'6" × 30'0" × 18'8½"	658	R. M. Sloman & Co.	Hamburg	1864
60	Iron S.S.	*Spartan*	170'0" × 22'6" × 13'6"	421	R. Little	Greenock	1864
61	Iron S.S.	*Clara*	160'0" × 21'0" × 12'1⅛"	346	Ben Simons	Glasgow	1864
62	Iron Sailer	—	Not built		J. H. Watt	Glasgow	—
63	Iron Sailer	*Newton*	155'6" × 30'0" × 18'8½"	658	R. M. Sloman & Co.	Hamburg	1864

* Converted to Shenandoah, Confederate cruiser.

Ships built by Alexander Stephen & Sons at Kelvinhaugh – continued

Yard No.	Type of Ship	Name of Ship	Dimensions	Builders' old Tonnage (gross*)	Built for	Owners' Port	Completed
64	Iron S.S.	*Roma*	200'0" × 25'0" × 16'6"	615	Handyside & Henderson	Glasgow	1864
65	W. & I. Sailer	*Leon Crespo*	170'0" × 29'6" × 18'3"	705	Bain Brothers	Dumbarton	1865
66	Iron Barque	*Tocopilla*	149'0" × 26'9" × 17'6"	506	Leon Jose & Co.	Bolivia	1865
67	W. & I. Barque	*Carmelita*	160'0" × 28'6" × 18'0"	626	Leon Jose & Co.	Bolivia	1865
68	Iron S.S.	*Hibernia*	270'0" × 33'6" × 22'2"	1492	Handyside & Henderson	Glasgow	1865
69	Iron Barge	*No. 1*	85'0" × 20'1¼" × 6'3"	154	Finlay, Campbell & Co.	London	1865
70	Iron Barge	*No. 2*	85'0" × 20'1¼" × 6'3"	154	Finlay, Campbell & Co.	London	1865
71	Iron Barge	*No. 3*	85'0" × 20'1¼" × 6'3"	154	Finlay, Campbell & Co.	London	1865
72	Iron Barge	*No. 4*	85'0" × 20'1¼" × 6'3"	154	Finlay, Campbell & Co.	London	1865
73	Iron Barge	*No. 5*	85'0" × 20'1¼" × 6'3"	154	Finlay, Campbell & Co.	London	1865
74	Iron Barge	*No. 6*	85'0" × 20'1¼" × 6'3"	154	Finlay, Campbell & Co.	London	1865
75	Iron Barge	*No. 7*	85'0" × 20'1¼" × 6'3"	154	Finlay, Campbell & Co.	London	1865
76	Iron Barge	*No. 8*	85'0" × 20'1¼" × 6'3"	154	Finlay, Campbell & Co.	London	1865
77	Iron Barge	*No. 9*	85'0" × 20'1¼" × 6'3"	154	Finlay, Campbell & Co.	London	1865
78	Iron Barge	*No. 10*	85'0" × 20'1¼" × 6'3"	154	Finlay, Campbell & Co.	London	1865
79	Iron Barge	*No. 11*	85'0" × 20'1¼" × 6'3"	154	Finlay, Campbell & Co.	London	1865
80	Iron Barge	*No. 12*	85'0" × 20'1¼" × 6'3"	154	Finlay, Campbell & Co.	London	1865
81	Iron S.S.	*Zeta*	185'0" × 28'0" × 18'0"	*734	H. Bath & Sons	Swansea	1865
82	Iron Barque	*Belle of the Clyde*	110'0" × 22'0" × 11'9"	249	George Eastee	Liverpool	1865
83	W. & I. Barque	*Fusi Yama*	165'0" × 28'0" × 17'0"	618	Killick, Martin & Co.	London	1865
84	W. & I. Barque	*Kappa*	155'0" × 27'0" × 17'6"	538	H. Bath & Sons	Swansea	1865
85	W. & I. Sailer	*Rohilla*	200'0" × 33'0" × 21'0"	1044	Finlay, Campbell & Co.	London	1865
86	Iron S.S.	*Valetta*	200'0" × 25'0" × 16'6"	615	Handyside & Henderson	Glasgow	1865

Ships built by Alexander Stephen & Sons at Kelvinhaugh – continued

Yard No.	Type of Ship	Name of Ship	Dimensions	Builders' old Tonnage (gross*)	Built for	Owners' Port	Completed
87	Iron S.S.	*Sarah Garcia*	170'0" × 22'6" × 13'8'	421	Ben Simons	Glasgow	1865
88	Iron S.S.	*Venezia*	200'0" × 25'0" × 16'6"	615	Handyside & Henderson	Glasgow	1865
89	Iron Barque	*Mineiro*	150'0" × 27'6'" × 17'0"	537	J. Hainsworth	Liverpool	1866
90	W. & I. Sailer	*William Davie*	185'0" × 31'6" × 19'6"	877	Albion Shipping Co.	Glasgow	1866
91	Iron S.S.	*Columbia*	280'0" × 33'6" × 22'2"	1390	Handyside & Henderson	Glasgow	1866
92	Iron S.S.	*Osaca*	175'0" × 27'6" × 15'2½"	700	J. Howden & Co.	Glasgow	1866
93	W. & I. S.S.	*Thomas Roys*	126'0" × 22'0" × 13'2"	290	Hannen & Melchior	Copenhagen	1866
94	Iron P.S.	*Topsy*	130'0" × 24'0" × 11'0"	440	J. & A. Allan	Glasgow	1866
95	Iron Sailer	*Abeona*	200'0" × 33'0" × 21'2½"	1044	J. & A. Allan	Glasgow	1867
96	Iron S.S.	*Arcadia*	210'0" × 26'0" × 17'6"	807	Handyside & Henderson	Glasgow	1866
97	W. & I. Schooner	*Metero*	120'0" × 26'0" × 9'0"	375	J. Hainsworth	Liverpool	1866
98	Iron Barge	*No. –*	40'0" × 13'0" × 5'0"	—	J. Hainsworth	Liverpool	1866
99	Iron Brig	*Annie Story*	165'0" × 28'0" × 18'6"	*591	R. G. Sharp	Maryport	1867
100	Iron Barque	*Pacific*	140'0" × 26'0" × 16'6"	447	W. R. Tremellen	Swansea	1867
101	Iron Sailer	*Humboldt*	165'0" × 30'0" × 18'8½"	*741	R. M. Sloman & Co.	Hamburg	1867
102	Iron Sailer	*Reichstag*	165'0" × 30'0" × 18'8½"	*737	R. M. Sloman & Co.	Hamburg	1867
103	Iron S.S.	*Europa*	280'0" × 33'6" × 22'2"	1390	Handyside & Henderson	Glasgow	1867
104	Iron S.S.	*Hannah Simons*	200'0" × 27'0" × 16'0"	713	Ben Simons	Glasgow	1867
105	Iron Sailer	*Grace Gibson*	162'0" × 27'3" × 17'10"	*548	H. W. Hewitt	Whitehaven	1867
106	W. & I. Sailer	*Omba*	185'0" × 37'9" × 19'0"	890	J. H. Watt	Glasgow	1868
107	Iron Barque	*Annie Richmond*	170'0" × 29'3" × 19'3"	*713	R. G. Sharp	Maryport	1868
108	W. & I. Barque	*Mary Moore*	160'0" × 28'0" × 18'0"	*585	J. Norman, Junr	Maryport	1868
109	Iron Barque	*Annie Main*	148'0" × 27'9" × 17'2¼"	545	T. Skinner	Glasgow	1867

Ships built by Alexander Stephen & Sons at Kelvinhaugh – continued

Yard No.	*Type of Ship*	*Name of Ship*	*Dimensions*	*Builders' old Tonnage (gross*)*	*Built for*	*Owners' Port*	*Completed*
110	W. & I. Sailer	*Forward Ho*	190'0" × 33'6" × 20'8½"	943	Joseph Hossack	Liverpool	1867
111	Iron Barque	*Limari*	167'0" × 27'8" × 18'6"	600	Thomas Connell	Whitehaven	1867
112	W. & I. Sailer	*Rona*	155'0" × 29'6" × 18'9"	638	Sandbach Tinne & Co.	Liverpool	1867
113	W. & I. Barque	*Lizzie Iredale*	170'0" × 31'0" × 18'5½"	693	Peter Iredale	Maryport	1868
114	Iron Schooner	*Janette*	82'0" × 19'0" × 9'2"	*91	Wm Couper & Co.	Glasgow	1867
115	Iron Sailer	*Centurion*	220'0" × 35'0" × 22'6"	1297	Captain James McKellar	Glasgow	1868
116	Iron Sailer	*Comadre*	185'0" × 31'0" × 19'6"	851	T. H. Ismay & Co.	Liverpool	1868
117	W. & I. Sailer	*Malacca*	165'0" × 29'0" × 17'8½"	594	James Graham & Co.	Liverpool	1868
118	W. & I. Sailer	*Singapore*	170'0" × 29' 9" × 17'11½"	656	T. H. Ismay & Co.	Glasgow	1869
119	Iron Barque	*Clydevale*	150'0" × 27'6" × 17'0"	*537	William Wylie	Glasgow	1868
120	W. & I. Sailer	*St Kilda*	187'0" × 32'6" × 19'3"	947	Sandbach Tinne & Co.	Liverpool	1868
121	Iron Barque	*Belle of Lagos*	125'0" × 24'0" × 11'9"	*251	George Eastee	Liverpool	1868
122	Iron Barque	*Atlantic*	150'0" × 27'6" × 17'0"	537	W. R. Tremellen	Swansea	1869
123	Iron Barque	*Caroline*	174'0" × 29'0" × 18'8"	687	Le Quellec & Bordes	Bordeaux	1869
124	Iron Barque	*Antonia*	174'0" × 29'0" × 18'8"	689	Le Quellec & Bordes	Bordeaux	1869
125	W. & I. Sailer	*City of Hankow*	220'0" × 36'0½" × 22'6"	1368	George Smith & Sons	Glasgow	1869
126	Iron Sailer	*Kildonan*	170'0" × 30'0" × 18'3'"	728	Wm Ross & Co.	Glasgow	1869
127	Iron Sailer	*City of Sparta*	223'0" × 35'0" × 22'6"	*1256	George Smith & Sons	Glasgow	1870
128	W. & I. Sailer	*Norham Castle*	175'0" × 32'0" × 18'2½"	698	T. Skinner & Black	Glasgow	1869
129	W. & I. Sailer	*Brechin Castle*	200'0" × 35'0" × 20'3"	1166	T. Skinner & Black	Glasgow	1869
130	Iron Sailer	*Friedeburg*	175'0" × 32'0" × 19'8½"	849	R. M. Sloman & Co.	Hamburg	1869
131	Iron Sailer	*Lammershagen*	175'0" × 32'0" × 19'8½"	849	R. M. Sloman & Co.	Hamburg	1869
132	Iron Barque	*Armin*	175'0'" × 32'0" × 19'8½"	849	D. H. Watjen & Co.	Bremen	1869

Ships built by Alexander Stephen & Sons at Kelvinhaugh – continued

Yard No.	*Type of Ship*	*Name of Ship*	*Dimensions*	*Builders' old Tonnage (gross*)*	*Built for*	*Owners' Port*	*Completed*
133	Iron Barque	*Henry Sempe*	148'0" × 27'9" × 17'2¼"	*492	P. Dumont & Co.	Bordeaux	1869
134	W.& I. S.S.	*Diana*	115'0" × 21'6'" × 12'7"	*189	J. Lamont	Toward	1869
135	Iron Sailer	*Anglia*	315'0'" × 35'0'" × 22'8½"	*2143	Handyside & Henderson	Glasgow	1869
136	Iron Barque	*Otago*[1]	140'0" × 26'0'" × 14'0"	*349	Angus Cameron	Glasgow	1869
137	Iron Sailer	*Sydenham*	200'0" × 34'0" × 21'3"	*1120	J. H. Luscombe	London	1870
138	Iron Schooner	*Aurora del Titicaca*	48'0" × 10'6" × 5'0"	70	A. Gibb & Sons	London	1869
139	W. & I. S.S.	*Stork*	160'0" × 23'0" × 11'2½"	*460	E. M. De Busshe	London	1869
140	Iron Sailer	*Maggie Trimble*	185'0" × 31'0" × 19'3"	*820	R. G. Sharp	Maryport	1870
141	Iron P.S.	*Countess of Kelly*	81'0" × 19'0" × 6'6"	210	Caledonian Railway Co.	Glasgow	1869
142	Iron Barque	*Valentine & Helene*	170'0" × 29'3" × 17'11½"	694	A. C. Le Quellec	Bordeaux	1870
143	Iron Barque	*Virginia*	177'0" × 32'0" × 19'8½"	*804	D. H. Watjen & Co.	Bremen	1870
144	W. & I. Barque	*Lima*	178'0" × 31'10" × 19'8½"	805	D. H. Watjen & Co.	Bremen	1870
145	Iron S.S.	*Atholl*	245'0" × 32'3 × 24'2½"	1395	J. Warrack & Co.	Leith	1870
146	Iron S.S.	*Shiraz*	230'0" × 29'6" × 23'9"	983	Gray, Dawes & Co.	London	1870
147	Iron S.S.	*Alert*	205'0" × 28'6" × 16'6"	*776	R. M. Sloman & Co.	Hamburg	1870

1. Commanded by Joseph Conrad. See *Shadow Line*.

Ships built by Alexander Stephen & Sons at Linthouse

Yard No.	Type of Ship	Name of Ship	Dimensions	Gross Tonnage	Built for	Owners' Port	Completed
148	S.S.	*Glendarroch*	265'0" × 33'0" × 24'6"	1509	Wm Ross & Company	Glasgow	1870
149	Barque	*Canopus*	182'0" × 32'6" × 21'9"	902	E. M. De Busshe	London	1870
150	S.S.	*Sunfoo*	255'0" × 33'0" × 24'3"	1449	E. M. De Busshe	London	1870
151	S.S.	*Glen Sannox*	265'0" × 33'0" × 24'6"	1500	Wm Ross & Company	Glasgow	1870
152	S.S.	*California*	360'0" × 40'0" × 31'10"	3434	Handyside & Henderson	Glasgow	1872
153	P.S.	*Para*	240'0" × 38'0" × 19'9½"	1543	Wm R. Garrison	New York	1871
154	P.S.	*Ceara*	240'0" × 38'0" × 19'9½"	1546	Wm R. Garrison	New York	1871
155	P.S.	*Bahia*	240'0" × 38'0" × 19'9½"	1539	Wm R. Garrison	New York	1871
156	S.S.	*Daqupon*	130'0" × 22'0" × 7'4"	169	Killick Martin & Co.	London	1871
157	Barque	*Anna*	175'0" × 32'0" × 21'6"	877	D. H. Watjen & Co.	Bremen	1871
158	S.S.	*Selicia*	230'0" × 31'0" × 17'7"	908	F. J. G. Servais	Antwerp	1872
159	Barque	*Josefa*	175'0" × 32'0" × 21'6"	875	D. H. Watjen & Co.	Bremen	1872
160	S.S.	*Nelusko**	320'0" × 36'0" × 27'0"	2279	F. J. G. Servais	Antwerp	1872
161	S.S.	*Muriel*	250'0" × 30'0" × 20'0"	1161	Blythe Brothers	Liverpool	1872
162	Barque	*Belle of the Niger*	141'0" × 25'0" × 11'8"	246	George Eastee	London	1872
163	S.S.	*Neapel*	205'0" × 28'6" × 16'8"	866	R. M. Sloman & Co.	Hamburg	1872
164	S.S.	*Tromp*	320'0" × 36'0" × 27'0"	2279	T. C. Engels & Co.	Antwerp	1873
165	S.S.	*Pow An*	220'0" × 34'0" × 12'10½"	2379	Fearon & Co.	London	1873
166	S.S.	*Ethiopia*	400'0" × 40'0" × 33'1"	4004	Handyside & Henderson	Glasgow	1873
167	S.S.	*Cassandra*	250'0" × 32'0" × 23'9½"	1434	John White, London	London	1873
168	S.S.	*Cybele*	320'0" × 34'6" × 25'3"	1980	Donaldson Brothers	Glasgow	1874

* First engine built at Linthouse.

Ships built by Alexander Stephen & Sons at Linthouse – continued

Yard No.	*Type of Ship*	*Name of Ship*	*Dimensions*	*Gross Tonnage*	*Built for*	*Owners' Port*	*Completed*
169	S.S.	*Herder*	375'0" × 40'0" × 32'2½"	3494	Deutsche Transatlantische	Hamburg	1873
170	S.S.	*Lessing*	375'0" × 40'0" × 32'2½"	3496	Dampschiffshalt	Hamburg	1874
171	S.S.	*Wieland*	375'0" × 40'0" × 32'2½"	3507	Gesellshaft	Hamburg	1874
172	S.S.	*Tambaroora*	160'0" × 24'0" × 14'0"	400	Leon Fernadas	Costa Rica	1875
173	S.S.	*Gellert*	375'0" × 40'3" × 32'0"	3536	D. T. D. G.	Hamburg	1875
174	S.S.	*Nepaul*	375'0" × 40'3" × 32'2½"	3536	P. & O. S. N. Co.	London	1876
175	S.S.	*Bruce*	170'0" × 22'0" × 10'3"	335	John Darling	Dunedin	1874
176	Barque	*Germania*	180'0" × 31'8" × 19'8"	861	D. H. Watjen & Co.	Bremen	1874
177	Barque	*G. Broughton*	190'0" × 31'9" × 18'10"	828	Peter Iredale	Carlisle	1874
178	Barque	*Britannia*	175'0" × 32'0" × 21'6"	881	D. H. Watjen & Co.	Bremen	1874
179	S.S.	*Euro*	165'0" × 23'0" × 10'6"	335	Capt. Wm Osborne	Adelaide	1874
180	Sail Ship	*Airlie*	235'0" × 38'2" × 24'5"	1577	David Bruce & Co.	Dundee	1875
181	Sail Ship	*Camperdown*	235'0" × 38'2" × 24'5"	1575	David Bruce & Co.	Dundee	1875
182	Sail Ship	*Panmure*	235'0" × 38'2" × 24'5"	1523	David Bruce & Co.	Dundee	1875
183	Schooner	*Osburgha*	140'0" × 26'0" × 13'8"	357	William Cook	London	1875
184	Barque	*Picton Castle*	165'0" × 28'0" × 17'10½"	596	Simpson Brothers	Swansea	1875
185	Barque	*Lord Clyde*	165'0" × 28'0" × 18'7"	591	Gilbert Tulloch	Swansea	1875
186	Barque	*Llewellyn*	155'0" × 27'6" × 17'3"	529	Captain John Rosser	Swansea	1875
187	Sail Ship	*Amana*	230'0" × 36'0" × 21'11"	1375	Captain John Smith	Glasgow	1875
188	Composite P.S.	*Mauricio*	108'0" × 19'0" × 9'11"	165	James Graham & Co.	London	1875
189	Barque	*Lady Penrhyn*	198'0" × 31'9" × 20'6"	839	J. Richards, M.D.	Bangor	1875
190	Barque	*Martha Fisher*	198'0" × 31'9" × 20'0"	839	Peter Iredale	Carlisle	1875
191	Barque	*Primera*	174'0" × 28'6" × 18'7"	597	William Sherwen	Liverpool	1875

Ships built by Alexander Stephen & Sons at Linthouse – continued

Yard No.	Type of Ship	Name of Ship	Dimensions	Gross Tonnage	Built for	Owners' Port	Completed
192	Barque	*Nokomis*	190'0" × 31'6" × 18'11"	881	W. McCorkell & Co.	Londonderry	1876
193	Barque	*Werra*	187'0" × 32'0" × 19'8½"	932	D. H. Watjen & Co.	Bremen	1876
194	Barque	*Fulda*	187'0" × 32'0" × 19'8½"	884	D. H. Watjen & Co.	Bremen	1876
195	Composite Barque	*India*	187'9" × 34'0" × 19'8½"	974	D. H. Watjen & Co.	Bremen	1876
196	P.S.	*City of Grafton*	207'0" × 27'0" × 19'6"	825	J. B. Watt & Co.	London	1876
197	Sail Ship	*Shenir*	215'0" × 34'9" × 23'3"	1229	Captain John Smith	Glasgow	1876
198	Sail Ship	*Pleione*	210'0" × 34'6" × 21'9"	1092	Shaw, Savill & Albion Co.	London	1876
199	Sail Ship	*Cockermouth*	239'0" × 36'9" × 22'9"	1297	Peter Iredale	Carlisle	1876
200	Sail Ship	*Ardencluthа*	220'0" × 35'6" × 21'6"	1293	J. L. Mitchell (Edmiston & Mitchell)	Glasgow	1876
201	Barque	*Einclune*	185'0"" × 30'0" × 19'8"	718	Dundee, Perth & London S. Co.	Dundee	1876
202	Barque	*Lochinvar*	185'0" × 30'0" × 19'8"	685	J. Boumphrey & Co.	Liverpool	1876
203	Sail Ship	*Opawa*	215'0" × 34'0" × 21'11"	1076	New Zealand Shipping Co.	London	1876
204	Sail Ship	*Piako*	215'0" × 34'0" × 21'10"	1075	New Zealand Shipping Co.	London	1876
205	Sail Ship	*Wanganui*	215'0" × 34'0" × 21'10"	1077	New Zealand Shipping Co.	London	1877
206	S.S.	*Leon*	197'0" × 26'6" × 14'0½"	621	Chevillotte Bros.	Brest	1876
207	Barque	*Lurline*	189'0" × 32'0" × 19'3"	761	Paton & Grant	Glasgow	1877
208	Barque	*Psyche*	205'0" × 34'0" × 20'3"	1031	A. C. Le Quellec	Bordeaux	1877
209	S.S.	*Brutus*	190'0" × 27'0"" × 15'9½"	628	Gebrüder Andersen	Kiel	1877
210	S.S.	*Pinzan*	201'6" × 28'2" × 18'2"	832	Robert McAndrew & Co.	London	1877
211	S.S.	*Solis*	201'6" × 28'2" × 18'2"	835	Robert McAndrew & Co.	London	1877
212	Barque	*River Leven*	178'0" × 32'2" × 18'8½"	806	Alex. Denny	Dumbarton	1877

Ships built by Alexander Stephen & Sons at Linthouse – continued

Yard No.	Type of Ship	Name of Ship	Dimensions	Gross Tonnage	Built for	Owners' Port	Completed
213	Ferry P.S.	Australian Ferry Steamer	116'0" × 15'6" × 7'5"	100	John Hay & Wm Buchanan	Ayr	1877
214	Barque	*Palala*	215'0" × 34'0" × 19'11"	1030	Bullard King & Co.	London	1878
215	Barque	*Mabel Young*	203'0" × 33'6" × 20'8½"	1046	Killick Martin & Co.	London	1878
216	Barque	*Visurgis*	207'6" × 34'6" × 20'3"	1141	D. H. Watjen & Co.	Bremen	1877
217	Barque	*Lesmona*	207'6" × 34'6" × 20'3"	1144	D. H. Watjen & Co.	Bremen	1877
218	S.S.	*Mercator*	280'0" × 35'0" × 26'0"	1958	T. C. Engels & Co.	Antwerp	1877
219	Barque	*George Knox*	138'0" × 27'0" × 13'8½"	349	George Knox	Natal	1877
220	S.S.	*Titus*	190'0" × 28'0" × 15'9½"	760	Gebrüder Andersen	Kiel	1878
221	S.S.	*Augustus*	236'0" × 31'0" × 19'0½"	1126	Gebrüder Andersen	Kiel	1878
222	T.S.S.	*Houssa*	192'0" × 26'0" × 13'1"	544	Alex. Miller Bros & Co.	Glasgow	1878
223	Barque	*Hannah Landles*	230'0" × 36'0" × 22'6½"	1332	David Law	Glasgow	1878
224	Barque	*Alice Platt*	208'0" × 34'0" × 21'11"	1139	J. Lloyd, Junr.	Bangor	1878
225	Barque	*Goethe*	217'6" × 34'6" × 21'7½"	1209	D. H. Watjen & Co.	Bremen	1878
226	S.S.	*Clan Alpine*	305'0" × 34'9" × 25'6½"	2080	Cayzer, Irvine & Co.	Liverpool	1878
227	S.S.	*Clan Fraser*	305'0" × 34'9" × 25'6½"	2083	Cayzer, Irvine & Co.	Liverpool	1878
228	S.S.	*Escurial*	230'0" × 30'0" × 23'4"	1185	Raeburn & Verel	Glasgow	1879
229	S.S.	*Claverhouse*	230'0" × 30'0" × 23'4"	1188	John Dunn & Co.	Glasgow	1879
230	S.S.	*Eileen Dubh*	100'0" × 18'0" × 8'7½"	111	Moray Firth Shipping Co.	Inverness	1879
231	S.S.	*Felicia*	236'0" × 31'0" × 19'0½"	1125	A. C. de Freitas & Co.	Hamburg	1878
232	S.S.	*Clan Gordon*	305'0" × 34'9" × 25'6½"	2091	Cayzer, Irvine & Co.	Liverpool	1879
233	S.S.	*Clan Lamont*	305'0" × 34'9" × 25'6½"	2091	Cayzer, Irvine & Co.	Liverpool	1879
234	Schooner	*Tabasco*	131'0" × 23'0" × 10'4"	215	Jenequel Frères	Bordeaux	1879

Ships built by Alexander Stephen & Sons at Linthouse – continued

Yard No.	Type of Ship	Name of Ship	Dimensions	Gross Tonnage	Built for	Owners' Port	Completed
235	T.S.S.	*Fantee*	120'0" × 18'0" × 19'0"	166	Alex. Miller Bros & Co.	Glasgow	1879
236	S.S.	*Claudius*	254'0" × 33'0" × 21'5½"	1454	C. Andersen	Hamburg	1879
237	S.S.	*Plantyn*	320'0" × 36'0" × 27'6½"	2328	T. C. Engels & Co.	Antwerp	1879
238	S.S.	*Malaga*	265'0" × 33'0" × 21'5"	1344	R. M. Sloman & Co.	Hamburg	1879
239	S.S.	*Barcelona*	265'0" × 33'0" × 21'5"	1346	R. M. Sloman & Co.	Hamburg	1879
240	S.S.	*Mobile*	250'0" × 32' 6" × 23'7"	1409	Capt. H. N. Herriman	U.S.A.	1879
241	S.S.	*Africa*	260'0" × 33'6" × 23'4"	1495	Edward Carr	Hamburg	1879
242	S.S.	*Vincenzo Florio*	340'0" × 38'0" × 30'4½"	2817	Nav. Gen. Italiana	Palermo	1880
243	S.S.	*Washington*	340'0" × 38'0" × 30'4½"	2814	Nav. Gen. Italiana	Palermo	1880
244	S.S.	*Lennox*	310'0" × 35'0" × 26'8"	2054	John Warrack & Co.	Leith	1880
245	S.S.	*Carlo*	240'0" × 34'0" × 18'6"	1271	Tellefsen Wills & Co.	Cardiff	1880
246	S.S.	*Earl of Rosebery*	240'0" × 33'2½" × 17'2"	1163	Martin & Marquand	Cardiff	1880
247	S.S.	*Benalder*	310'0" × 35'0" × 26'8"	2054	Wm Thomson & Co.	Leith	1880
248	S.S.	*Katie*	320'0" × 40'6" × 26'0"	2450	C. H. S. Schultz	Hamburg	1880
249	S.S.	*Mount Hermon*	320'0" × 38'0" × 27'6"	2410	Captain John Smith	Glasgow	1880
250	S.S.	*Alverton*	240'0" × 34'0" × 18'6"	1321	Osborn & Wallis	Cardiff	1880
251	S.S.	*Mount Lebanon*	320'0" × 38'0" × 27'6"	2410	Captain John Smith	Glasgow	1881
252	S.S.	*Pieter de Connick*	340'0" × 40'9" × 34'3'"	3310	T. C. Engels & Co.	Antwerp	1881
253	S.S.	*Catania*	315'0" × 35'6" × 25'10"	2198	R. M. Sloman & Co.	Hamburg	1881
254	S.S.	*Fidra*	237'8" × 33'0" × 19'1"	1139	Francis F. Reid	Leith	1881
255	S.S.	*Iniziativa*	300'0" × 37'3" × 26'3"	2032	Carlo Raggio	Genoa	1881
256	S.S.	*Pallas*	192'0" × 26'0" × 14'9½"	595	Wm Jex & Co.	London	1881
257	S.S.	*Cameo*	300'0" × 39'0" × 26'7½"	2280	Tellefsen, Wills & Co.	Cardiff	1881

Ships built by Alexander Stephen & Sons at Linthouse – continued

Yard No.	Type of Ship	Name of Ship	Dimensions	Gross Tonnage	Built for	Owners' Port	Completed
258	S.S.	*Archimede*	340'0" × 40'0" × 28'10"	2837	Nav. Gen. Italiana	Rome	1881
259	S.S.	*Benlarig*	310'0" × 38'0" × 26'6"	2265	W. Thomson & Co.	Leith	1881
260	S.S.	*Sorrento*	320'0" × 36'0" × 25'10"	2370	R. M. Sloman & Co.	Hamburg	1881
261	S.S.	*Clan Cameron*	324'0" × 38'0" × 26'9½"	2432	Cayzer, Irvine & Co.	Liverpool	1882
262	S.S.	*Clan Campbell*	324'0" × 38'0" × 26'9½"	2433	Cayzer, Irvine & Co.	Liverpool	1882
263	S.S.	*Clan Forbes*	324'0" × 38'0" × 26'9½"	2441	Cayzer, Irvine & Co.	Liverpool	1882
264	S.S.	*Clan Ogilvie*	324'0" × 38'0" × 26'9½"	2425	Cayzer, Irvine & Co.	Liverpool	1882
265	S.S.	*Marsala*	320'0" × 36'0" × 25'10"	2370	R. M. Sloman & Co.	Hamburg	1882
266	S.S.	*Mudela*	260'0" × 38'0" × 20'1"	1711	J. Martinez de la Rivas	Bilbao	1882
267	S.S.	*Albany*	310'0" × 38'0" × 26'8"	2276	John Warrack & Co.	Leith	1882
268	S.S.	*Independente*	340'0" × 40'0" × 28'10"	2836	Nav. Gen. Italiana	Palermo	1883
269	S.S.	*Gottardo*	340'0" × 40'0" × 28'10'"	2836	Nav. Gen. Italiana	Palermo	1883
270	Barque	*Aberdeenshire*	230'0" × 36'0" × 22'6½"	1340	Thomas Law & Co.	Glasgow	1882
271	S.S.	*Rosslyn*	270'0" × 34'3" × 23'1"	1615	John Warrack & Co.	Leith	1882
272	S.S.	*Clan Grant*	350'0" × 41'0" × 27'9"	3545	Cayzer, Irvine & Co.	Liverpool	1883
273	Barque	*Teviotdale*	255'0" × 38'6" × 24'3½"	1695	J. & A. Roxburgh	Glasgow	1882
274	S.S.	*Benvenue*	310'0" × 38'0" × 26'6"	2286	Wm Thomson & Co.	Leith	1883
275	S.Y.	*Sylvia*	125'0" × 18'0" × 10'10½"	136	Dean of Guild Stephen	Glasgow	1882
276	S.S.	*Marques de Mudela*	280'0" × 38'0" × 24'9½"	1913	J. Martinez de la Rivas	Bilbao	1883
277	S.S.	*Cymro*	300'0" × 39'0" × 26'7½"	2280	Tellefsen, Wills & Co.	Cardiff	1883
278	S.S.	*Graville*	300'0" × 39'0" × 26'7½"	2397	Cicero Brown	Le Havre	Oct. 1883
279	S.S.	*Rose (Daphne)*	176'3" × 25'2" × 21'2½"	449	Glasgow & Londonderry S.P. Co. (Laird Line)	Glasgow	Sept. 1883

Yard No.	*Type of Ship*	*Name of Ship*	*Dimensions*	*Gross Tonnage*	*Built for*	*Owners' Port*	*Completed*
280	S.S.	*Euterpe*	260'0" × 36'0" × 19'1½"	1522	Osborn & Wallis	Cardiff	Oct. 1883
281	S.S.	*Clan Davidson*	240'0" × 34'0" × 18'6"	1326	Thos Dunlop & Sons	Glasgow	Dec. 1883
282	S.S.	*Ella*	220'0" × 31'0" × 17'5"	1058	Theodore Rodenacker	Dantzig	Dec. 1883
283	S.S.	*Taormina*	320'0" × 38'6" × 26'8"	2422	R. M. Sloman & Co.	Hamburg	March 1884
284	S.S.	*Dunedin*	240'0" × 34'0" × 18'6"	1326	Henderson & McIntosh	Leith	March 1884
285	Barque	*Galathee*	220'0" × 36'0" × 21'11½"	1253	A. C. Le Quellec	Bordeaux	May 1884
286	S.S.	*Rivas*	300'0" × 42'0" × 28'2½"	2700	J. Martinez de la Rivas	Bilbao, Spain	Sept. 1884
287	Schooner	*Tampico*	131'0" × 24'0" × 11'10½"	309	Jenequel Frères	Bordeaux	July 1884
288	Barque	*Edinburghshire*	230'0" × 36'0" × 22'6½"	1343	Thomas Law & Co.	Glasgow	Oct. 1884
289	Sail Ship	*Ardencaple*	255'0" × 39'6" × 25'0"	1782	Robert Lockhart	Glasgow	Jan. 1885
290	S.S.	*Damara*	275'0" × 35'0" × 23'11"	1779	Halifax S. Nav. Co.	Nova Scotia	March 1885
291	S.S.	*Ulanda*	275'0" × 35'0" × 23'11"	1789	Halifax S. Nav. Co.	Nova Scotia	May 1885
292	Barque	*Abercorn*	230'0" × 36'0" × 22'6½"	1341	P. H. Dixon & Co.	Glasgow	April 1885
293	Sail Ship	*Brynhilda*	232'0" × 38'0" × 23'3¾"	1502	J. W. Carmichael & Co.	New Glasgow, Nova Scotia	May 1885
294	S.Y.	*Nerissa*	147'0" × 22'0" × 13'6"	264	Alexander Stephen	Glasgow	June 1885
295	S.S.	*Wardha*	350'0" × 47'0" × 29'5"	3917	British India S. N. Co.	London	July 1887
296	S.S.	*Warora*	350'0" × 47'0" × 29'5"	3920	British India S. N. Co.	London	Sept. 1887
297	S.S.	*General Gordon*	240'0" × 34'0" × 18'6"	1294	Maclay & McIntyre	Glasgow	Sept. 1885
298	Sail Ship	*Circe*	240'0" × 39'6" × 23'11½"	1650	A. C. Le Quellec	Bordeaux	Nov. 1885
299	S.S.	*Queen Victoria*	290'0" × 39'0" × 25'3½"	2311	Thos. Dunlop & Sons	Glasgow	Jan. 1887
300	S.S.	*Bléville*	300'0" × 40'0" × 25'9"	2518	C. Brown	Havre	Sept. 1886
301	Barque	*Kilfauns*	197'0" × 34'6" × 20'8½"	1007	C. Couper	Dundee	Oct. 1886

Ships built by Alexander Stephen & Sons at Linthouse – continued

Yard No.	Type of Ship	Name of Ship	H.P.	Dimensions	Gross Tonnage	Built for	Owners' Port	Completed
302	Sail Ship	*Armadale*	—	275'0" × 40'6" × 25'3½"	2015	J. & A. Roxburgh	Glasgow	April 1887
303	Sail Ship	*Bracadale*	—	275'0" × 40'6" × 25'3½"	2015	J. & A. Roxburgh	Glasgow	May 1887
304	S.S.	*Gairloch*	—	282'0" × 37'0" × 21'9"	2173	James Gardiner & Co.	Glasgow	Sept. 1887
305	S.S.	*Vascongada*	—	250'0" × 35'0" × 19'4½"	1483	Ferguson & Reid	Glasgow	Oct. 1887
306	S.S.	*Elettrico*	—	250'0" × 33'0" × 23'10½"	1246	Nav. Gen. Italiana	Rome	Aug. 1887
307	S.S.	*Victoria*	—	260'0" × 36'9" × 19'2"	1620	Maclay & McIntyre	Glasgow	Oct. 1887
308	S.S.	*Strathearn*	—	310'0" × 41'2¼" × 27'9"	2814	Burrell & Son	Glasgow	Feb. 1888
309	S.S.	*Caloric*	—	260'0" × 36'9" × 19'2"	1747	Ebenezer Kemp	Glasgow	Jan. 1888
310	S.S.	*Domira*	—	260'0" × 36'9" × 19'2"	1791	Maclay & McIntyre	Glasgow	April 1888
311	S.S.	*Baltimore City*	—	290'0" × 39'0" × 25'3½"	2334	C. Furness	W. Hartlepool	May 1888
312	S.S.	*Kentigern*	—	300'0" × 40'0" × 25'9"	2463	R. McMillan	Dumbarton	July 1888
313	S.S.	*Amaranth*	—	310'0" × 40'0" × 27'3½"	2677	J. B. Murray & Co.	Glasgow	Sept. 1888
314	S.S.	*Queen Elizabeth*	—	300'0" × 40'0" × 25'9"	2507	Thos. Dunlop & Sons	Glasgow	Nov. 1888
315	S.S.	*Strathclyde*	—	340'0" × 45'5¼" × 26'9½"	3265	Burrell & Son	Glasgow	March 1889
316	Sail Ship	*Carr Rock*	—	240'0" × 39'0" × 23'9"	1657	Jas Cornfoot & Co.	Glasgow	Jan. 1889
317	S.S.	*Capua*	1150	285'0" × 37'0" × 23'8½"	2012	R. M. Sloman & Co.	Hamburg	May 1889
318	S.S.	*Salerno*	1061	285'0" × 37'0" × 23'8½"	2012	R. M. Sloman & Co.	Hamburg	Sept. 1889
319	S.S.	*Nyassa*	980	280'0" × 37'3" × 21'9"	2202	Maclay & McIntyre	Glasgow	June 1889
320	S.S.	*Mangara*	817	260'0" × 36'9" × 19'2"	1784	Maclay & McIntyre	Glasgow	June 1889
321	Sail Ship	*Carradale*	—	275'0" × 41'0" × 25'3½"	2085	J. & A. Roxburgh	Glasgow	Nov. 1889
322	S.S.	*Chemnitz*	1563	320'0" × 39'0" × 25'6"	2700	German Australian Co.	Hamburg	Dec. 1889
323	Sail Ship	*Fascadale*	—	275'0" × 41'0" × 25'3½"	2085	J. & A. Roxburgh	Glasgow	Feb. 1890
324	S.S.	*Highland Chief*	1510	310'0" × 41'0" × 26'3"	2648	Maclay & McIntyre	Glasgow	May 1890

Ships built by Alexander Stephen & Sons at Linthouse – continued

Yard No.	Type of Ship	Name of Ship	H.P.	Dimensions	Gross Tonnage	Built for	Owners' Port	Completed
325	S.S.	*Asphodel*	1340	310'0" × 41' 0" × 26'3"	2674	J. B. Murray & Co.	Glasgow	May 1890
326	S.S.	*Queen Margaret*	1475	310'0" × 41 ' 0" × 26'3"	2678	Thos Dunlop & Sons	Glasgow	May 1890
327	S.S.	*Ben Lomond*	1596	310'0" × 40'0" × 26'9"	2670	Wm Thomson & Co.	Leith	July 1890
328	S.S.	*Boston*	4763	245'0" × 36'1½" × 21'0"	1694	Yarmouth S.S. Co.	Nova Scotia	Oct. 1890
329	S.S.	*State of California*	4315	385'0" × 46' 0" × 32'8"	4244	State of California Co.	Glasgow	Aug. 1891
330	S.S.	*Ottawa*	1530	275'0" × 35'0" × 23'11"	1719	C. Furness	W. Hartlepool	Feb. 1891
331	S.S.	*Acanthus*	1562	310'0" × 42'0" × 25'6"	2877	J. B. Murray & Co.	Glasgow	March 1891
332	S.S.	*Clan Mackinnon*	2036	295'0" × 39'0" × 24'9"	2268	Cayzer, Irvine & Co.	Glasgow	May 1891
333	S.S.	*Clan Macnab*	1955	295'0" × 39'0" × 24' 9"	2268	Cayzer, Irvine & Co.	Glasgow	June 1891
334	S.S.	*Clan Macallister*	1917	295'0" × 39'0" × 24'9"	2268	Cayzer, Irvine & Co.	Glasgow	Aug. 1891
335	Barque	*Urania*	—	245'0" × 39'0" × 23'8"	1688	Telef Lassen	Arendal, Norway	Oct. 1891
336	Barque	*Afon Alaw*	—	275'0" × 41'0" × 25'3½"	2052	Hughes & Co.	Menai Bridge, N. Wales	Dec. 1891
337	S.S.	*Camelot*	1840	300'0" × 42'0" × 28'6"	2881	Francis F. Reid	Leith	April 1892
338	S.S.	*Uganda*	1323	310'0" × 41'0" × 24'6"	2444	Maclay & McIntyre	Glasgow	May 1892
339	Barque	*Afon Cefni**	—	275'0" × 41'0" × 25'3½"	2066	Hughes & Co.	Menai Bridge, N. Wales	April 1892
340	S.S.	*Bezwada*	1956	400'0" × 48'0" × 31'6"	5000	British India S. N. Co.	London	May 1893
341	S.S.	*Agapanthus*	1760	380'0" × 46'0"x 30'3"	4409	J. B. Murray & Co.	Glasgow	Jan. 1893
342	S.S.	*Durward* (No. 1)	2370	260'0" × 32'6" × 17'5½"	1274	G. Gibson & Co.	Leith	July 1892
343	S.S.	*Arabistan*	1904	325'0" × 32'6" × 29'6"	3193	F. C. Strick & Co.	London	April 1893

* Last sailing ship built at Linthouse.

Ships built by Alexander Stephen & Sons at Linthouse – continued

Yard No.	Type of Ship	Name of Ship	H.P.	Dimensions	Gross Tonnage	Built for	Owners' Port	Completed
344	S.S.	*Rappahannock*	3110	370'0" × 44'0" × 31'6"	3884	Chesapeake & Ohio S.S. Co.	London	Aug. 1893
345	S.S.	*Shenandoah*	3122	370'0" × 44'0" × 31'6"	3886	Chesapeake & Ohio S.S. Co.	London	Oct. 1893
346	S.S.	*Kanawha*	1660	370'0" × 44'0" × 31'6	3886	Chesapeake & Ohio S.S. Co.	London	Dec. 1893
347	S.S.	*Benmohr*	1850	330'0" × 41'9" × 27'0"	3000	Wm Thomson & Co.	Leith	Nov. 1893
348	S.S.	*Halifax City*	1650	300'0" × 37'0" × 25'9"	2141	Furness Withy & Co.	W. Hartlepool	Feb. 1894
349	S.S.	*Mazagon*	1138	400'0" × 48'0" × 31'6"	4997	P. & O. S.N. Co.	London	July 1894
350	S.S.	*Janeta*	1766	330'0" × 43'0" × 29'0"	3302	Maclay & McIntyre	Glasgow	April 1894
351	S.S.	*Jeanara*	1894	330'0" × 43'0" × 29'0	3302	Maclay & McIntyre	Glasgow	June 1894
352	S.S.	*Turkistan*	1750	345'0" × 47'0" × 29'6"	4060	F. C. Strick & Co.	London	Aug. 1894
353	S.S.	*Dionée*	1348	300'0" × 40' 0" × 26'6"	2471	A. C. Le Quellec	Bordeaux	Dec. 1894
354	S.S.	*Julia Park*	1585	330'0" × 43'4" × 25'11"	3085	J. Smith Park	Glasgow	Oct. 1894
355	S.S.	*Marthara*	1398	300'0" × 42'0" × 23'0"	2397	Maclay & McIntyre	Glasgow	Dec. 1894
356	S.S.	*St John City*	2016	300'0" × 37' 0" × 25'9"	2153	C. Furness	W. Hartlepool	Jan. 1895
357	S.S.	*Durward* (No.2)	2349	260'0" × 32'6" × 17'5½"	1304	G. Gibson & Co.	Leith	Feb. 1895
358	S.S.	*Benalder*	1925	330'0" × 41'9" × 27'0"	3044	Wm Thomson & Co.	Leith	April 1895
359	S.S.	*Sumatra*	3436	400'0" × 46'8½" × 31'0"	4607	P. & O. S.N. Co.	London	Aug. 1895
360	S.S.	*Oceana*	1444	330'0" × 45'0" × 28'9"	3530	Maclay & McIntyre	Glasgow	Sept. 1895
361	S.S.	*Magdala*	1494	330'0" × 45'0" × 28'9"	3512	Maclay & McIntyre	Glasgow	Nov. 1895
362	S.S.	*Idaho* (*London City*)	4808	450'0" × 49'0" × 34'3"	5531	T. Wilson, Sons & Co.	Hull	April 1896
363	S.S.	*Grenada*	2012	281'0" × 39'0" × 25'6"	2158	Geo. Christall	New York	Jan. 1896
364	S.S.	*Megantic*	5010	450'0" × 49' 0" × 34'3"	5531	Wilson & Furness – Leyland Line	London	May 1896

Ships built by Alexander Stephen & Sons at Linthouse – continued

Yard No.	Type of Ship	Name of Ship	H.P.	Dimensions	Gross Tonnage	Built for	Owners' Port	Completed
365	S.S.	*Benvorlich*	1940	345'0" × 43'3" × 27'6"	3381	Wm Thomson & Co.	Leith	June 1896
366	S.S.	*Clan Chisholm*	2093	312'0" × 40'2½" × 26'2"	2647	Cayzer, Irvine & Co.	Glasgow	July 1896
367	S.S.	*Clan Ogilvy*	2104	312'0" × 40'2½" × 26'2	2647	Cayzer, Irvine & Co.	Glasgow	Sept. 1897
368	S.S.	*Lakmé*	1893	330'0" × 43'2½" × 27'2"	3110	A. C. Le Quellec	Bordeaux	Oct. 1896
369	S.S.	*Pisa*	2528	390'0" × 46'0" × 30'6"	4473	R. M. Sloman & Co.	Hamburg	Dec. 1896
370	S.S.	*Nyanza*	1713	370'0" × 48'0" × 27'6"	4053	Maclay & McIntyre	Glasgow	Jan. 1897
371	S.S.	*Sahara*	1667	370'0" × 48'0" × 27'6"	4089	Maclay & McIntyre	Glasgow	April 1897
372	S.S.	*Alexandra*	4989	475'0" × 52'3" × 34'6"	6919	Wilson & Furness – Leyland Line	London	Oct. 1897
373	S.S.	*Boadicea*	4960	486'0" × 52'3" × 34'6"	7057	Wilson & Furness – Leyland Line	London	Jan. 1898
374	S.S.	*Viscaina*	1180	290'0" × 42'9" × 21'10"	2191	Ferguson & Reid	Glasgow	July 1897
375	S.S.	*Uganda*	2274	410'0" × 50'9" × 31'9"	5366	British India S.N. Co.	London	May 1898
376	S.S.	*Umta*	2280	410'0" × 50'9" × 31'9	5366	British India S.N. Co.	London	June 1898
377	S.S.	*Bengalia*	4093	485'0" × 57'0" × 36'0"	7690	Sir C. Furness (Sold to Hamburg-Amerika Line)	W. Hartlepool	Oct. 1898
378	S.S.	*Induna*	1564	380'0" × 49'11⅜" × 28'2¾"	4426	Maclay & McIntyre	Glasgow	Nov. 1898
379	S.Y.	*Calanthe*	841	157'0" × 24'0" × 14'3"	351	Alex. Stephen	Glasgow	June 1898
380	S.S.	*Bethania*	5018	485'0" × 57'0" × 36'0"	7519	Sir C. Furness (Sold to Hamburg-Amerika Line)	W. Hartlepool	March 1899
381	S.S.	*Clan Macaulay*	1588	326'0" × 40'2½" × 26'2½"	2834	Cayzer, Irvine & Co.	Glasgow	April 1899
382	S.S.	*Clan Maclaren*	1593	326'0" × 40'2½" × 26' 2½"	2834	Cayzer, Irvine & Co.	Glasgow	June 1899
383	T.S.S.	Montezuma	4384	485'0" × 59'0" × 33'6"	7345	Elder Dempster & Co.	Liverpool	Sept. 1899

Ships built by Alexander Stephen & Sons at Linthouse – continued

Yard No.	*Type of Ship*	*Name of Ship*	*H.P.*	*Dimensions*	*Gross Tonnage*	*Built for*	*Owners' Port*	*Completed*
384	T.S.S.	*Tunisian*	7906	500'0" × 59'3" × 43'0"	10756	Allan Line S.S. Co.	Glasgow	March 1900
385	S.S.	*Clan Maclachlan*	2551	395'0" × 48'0" × 30'0"	4729	Cayzer, Irvine & Co.	Glasgow	April 1900
386	S.S.	*Bohemian*	4789	511'0" × 58'3" × 45'0"	8548	F. Leyland & Co.	Liverpool	Aug. 1900
387	S.S.	*Port Morant**	5872	320'0" × 40'0" × 27'11½"	2831	Elder Dempster & Co.	Liverpool	Feb. 1901
388	—	Spanish Ship House	—	—	—	Senor Felix de Chavarri	Spain	Feb. 1902
389	S.S.	*Evangeline*	3460	360'0" × 45'2½" × 30'6"	3900	Furness, Withy & Co.	London	Oct. 1900
390	S.S.	*Loyalist*	3502	360'0" × 45'2½" × 30'6"	3904	Furness, Withy & Co.	London	Jan. 1901
391	T.S.S.	*Syria*	4738	450'0" × 52'2¾" × 33'6"	6660	P. & O. S.N. Co.	London	June 1901
392	S.S.	*Inkum*	2431	392'0" × 50 0" × 38'10"	4747	J. H. Welsford & Co. Ltd.	London	Aug. 1901
393	T.S.S.	*Oscar II*	9463	500'0" × 58'3" × 40'9"	9956	Det Forenede Dampskib-Selskab	Copenhagen	Feb. 1902
394	S.S.	*Burutu*	3137	360'0" × 44'2½" × 26'0"	3863	Elder Dempster & Co.	Liverpool	May 1902
395	S.S.	*Tarquah*	3095	360'0" × 44'2½" × 26'0"	3859	Elder Dempster & Co.	Liverpool	June 1902
396	S.S.	*Wyandra*	3809	340'0" × 46'0" × 28'0"	4058	Australasian U.S.N. Co.	Sydney	Sept.1902
397	Triple Turb. Yacht	*Emerald*	1640	203'0" × 28'8" × 18'6"	694	Sir Christopher Furness	London	April 1903
398	S.S.	*Massilia*	2796	400'0" × 49'2½" × 30'9"	5353	Anchor Line	Glasgow	Sept. 1902
399	T.S.S.	*Hellig Olav*	9610	500'0" × 58'3" × 40'9"	10072	Det Forenede Dampskib-Selskab	Copenhagen	March 1903
400	T.S.S.	*United States*	9600	500'0" × 58'3" × 40'9"	10082	Det Forenede Dampskib-Selskab	Copenhagen	May 1903

* Lengthened 30'0" on stocks.

Ships built by Alexander Stephen & Sons Ltd, at Linthouse – continued

Yard No.	*Type of Ship*	*Name of Ship*	*H.P.*	*Dimensions*	*Gross Tonnage*	*Built for*	*Owners' Port*	*Completed*
401	T.S.S.	*Miltiades*	8156	442'0" × 55'0" × 33'1"	6765	Aberdeen Line	London and	Oct. 1903
				Lengthened 50'0"	7827	(G. Thompson & Co.)	Aberdeen	March 1912
402	T.S.S.	*Marathon*	8182	442'0" × 55'0" × 33'1"	6765	Aberdeen Line	London and	Dec. 1903
				Lengthened 50'0"	7827	(G. Thompson & Co.)	Aberdeen	Oct. 1912
403	T.S.S.	*Port Kingston*	10284	460'0" × 55'6" × 36'0"	7585	Elder Dempster & Co.	Liverpool	July 1904
404	S. Tug	*Cruiser*	660	105'0" × 21'1" × 11'9"	167	Steel & Bennie Ltd.	Glasgow	April 1904
405	Trip. Turb.	*Virginian*	13200	520'0" × 60'3" × 41'2"	10754	Allan Line S.S. Co.	Glasgow	March 1905
406	S.S.	*Karina*	4070	370'0" × 46'2½" × 26'0"	4230	Elder Dempster & Co.	Liverpool	June 1905
407	S.S.	*Mendi*	4085	370'0" × 46'2½" × 26'0"	4222	Elder Dempster & Co.	Liverpool	July 1905
408	S.Y.	*Medea*	254	105'0" × 16'7¼" × 10'0"	112	Capt. W. Macallister Hall	Torrisdale Castle	Aug. 1904
409	S.S.	*Nicoya*	3617	365'0" × 46'2½" × 32'6"	3911	Elders & Fyffes, Ltd.	London	April 1905
410	S.S.	*Eildon*	2128	260'0" × 34'2" × 18'7½"	608	G. Gibson & Co.	Leith	Oct. 1905
411	S.S.	*Uganda*	2647	385'0" × 50'0" × 28'8"	4257	Maclay & McIntyre	Glasgow	Sept. 1905
412	S.S.	*Livingstonia*	2695	385'0" × 50'0" × 28'8"	4294	Maclay & McIntyre	Glasgow	Dec. 1905
413	S.S.	*Albertville*	4219	380'0" × 47'6¼" × 33'9"	4793	C. Belge Maritime du Congo	Antwerp	July 1906
414	S.S.	*Falaba*	4270	380'0" × 47'6¼" × 33'9"	4806	Elder Dempster & Co.	Liverpool	Oct. 1906
415	S.S.	*Barranco*	3644	372'0" × 47'8½" × 32'6"	4124	Elders & Fyffes	London	April 1906
416	S.S.	*Crown of Galicia*	2920	400'0" × 52'0" × 29'9"	4821	Prentice, Service and Henderson	Glasgow	Oct. 1906
417	S.S.	*Ormiston*	2947	400'0" × 52'0" × 29'9"	4843	R. & C. Allan	Glasgow	April 1907
418	S. Tug	*Victor*	797	106'0" × 22'1" × 11'0"	175	Steel & Bennie	Glasgow	May 1906
419	S.S.	*Cooma*	3832	330'0" × 46'0" × 32'3"	3839	Howard Smith Co.	Sydney	March 1907

Ships built by Alexander Stephen & Sons Ltd, at Linthouse – continued

Yard No.	*Type of Ship*	*Name of Ship*	*H.P.*	*Dimensions*	*Gross Tonnage*	*Built for*	*Owners' Port*	*Completed*
420	S.S.	*Janeta*	2715	385'0" × 50'0" × 28'8"	4271	Maclay & McIntyre	Glasgow	Nov. 1906
421	S.S.	*Kazembe*	2914	400'0" × 50'0" × 29'10"	4658	Bucknall S.S. Line	London	April 1907
422	T.S.S.	*Grampian*	7930	485'0" × 60'3" × 41'3½"	9598	Allan Line S.S. Co.	Glasgow	Sept. 1907
423	T.S.S.	*Oceania*	3797	390'0" × 50'0" × 33'9"	5368	Fratelli Cosulich	Trieste	Nov. 1907
424	T.S.S.	*Wyreema*	6926	400'0" × 54'2⅝" × 33'3"	6338	Australasian U.S.N. Co.	London and Sydney	Feb. 1908
425	T.S.S.	*Hesperian*	8199	485'0" × 60'3" × 41'3½"	9599	Allan Line S.S. Co.	Glasgow	April 1908
426	T.S.S.	*Makura*	9603	450'0" × 57'8¾' × 34'9"	8075	Union S.S. Co. of N.Z.	London	Sept. 1908
427	T.S.S.	*Bruxellesville*	5785	400'0" × 52'2⅜" × 35'3"	5799	C. Belge Maritime du Congo	Antwerp	April 1909
428	T.S.S.	*Mourilyan*	2127	220'0" × 36'1¾" × 19'6"	1349	Howard Smith Co.	Sydney	Aug. 1908
429	S.S.	*Koombana*	3953	340'0" × 48'2¼" × 23'6"	4399	Adelaide S.S. Co.	Adelaide	Dec. 1908
430	T.S.S.	*Hollandia*	5200	420'0" × 54'2¾" × 37'6"	7291	Koninklijke Hollandsche Lloyd	Amsterdam	March 1909
431	Racing Yacht	*Coila II*	—	6 Metre International Class	—	F. J. Stephen	Glasgow	May 1909
432	S.S.	*Tortuguero*	3790	374'0" × 47'8½" × 32'6"	4161	Elders & Fyffes	London	April 1909
433	S.S.	*Romera*	2642	401'10" × 52'2¾" × 29'10"	4949	Maclay & McIntyre	Glasgow	Aug. 1909
434	S.S.	*Masunda*	2757	401'10" × 52'2¾" × 29'10"	4952	Maclay & McIntyre	Glasgow	Sept. 1909
435	T.S.S.	*Levuka*	7560	400'0" × 55'0" × 33'3"	6129	Australasian U.S.N. Co.	London and Sydney	April 1910
436	T.S.S.	*Zeelandia*	6213	440'0" × 55'9" × 37'0"	7958	Koninklijke Hollandsche Lloyd	Amsterdam	June 1909
437	S.S.	*Damara*	2437	401'10" × 52'2¾" × 29'10"	4988	Maclay & McIntyre	Glasgow	June 1909

Ships built by Alexander Stephen & Sons Ltd, at Linthouse – continued

Yard No.	*Type of Ship*	*Name of Ship*	*H.P.*	*Dimensions*	*Gross Tonnage*	*Built for*	*Owners' Port*	*Completed*
438	T.S.S.	*Elisabethville*	6400	415'0" × 55'3" × 36'6"	7034	C. Belge Maritime du Congo	Antwerp	Dec. 1909
439	T.S.S.	*Abhona*	8950	390'0" × 50'2½" × 32'6"	4066	British India S.N. Co.	London	Nov. 1909
440	T.S.S.	*Ellenga*	7000	410'0" × 52'6" × 35'3"	5196	British India S.N. Co.	London	March 1911
441	S.S.	*Manzanares*	3750	376'0" × 48'3" × 32'0"	4094	Elders & Fyffes	London	April 1911
442	T.S.S.	*Ellora*	7000	410'0" × 52'6" × 35'3"	5201	British India S.N. Co.	London	June 1911
443	S.S.	*Clan Macnaughton*	4750	430'0" × 53'6" × 37'0"	4985	Cayzer, Irvine & Co.	Glasgow	Aug. 1911
444	S.S.	*Anchoria*	4200	410'0" × 53'3" × 32'6"	5430	Anchor Line	Glasgow	Sept. 1911
445	S.S.	*Media*	4200	410'0" × 53'3" × 32'6"	5437	Anchor Line	Glasgow	Nov. 1911
446	S. Tug	*Campaigner*	700	107'0" × 23'1" × 11'0"	163	Steel & Bennie	Glasgow	June 1911
447	T.S.S.	*El Uruguayo*	7400	440'0" × 58'11" × 38'0"	8361	Furness Withy & Co.	London	April 1912
448	S.S.	*Mascara*	2330	402'0" × 52'3" × 29'11"	4957	Maclay & McIntyre	Glasgow	March 1912
449	T.S.S.	*Aronda*	8906	390'0" × 50'2" × 32'6"	4062	British India S.N. Co.	London	May 1912
450	T.S.S.	*Anversville*	6940	440'0" × 55'9" × 37'0"	7645	C. Belge Maritime du Congo	Antwerp	Aug. 1912
451	T.S.S.	*Chagres* (1st)	5298	400'0" × 51'3" × 32'3"	5288	Elders & Fyffes	London	Sept. 1912
452	T.S.S.	*Canberra*	8269	410'0" × 57'3" × 33'3"	7707	Howard Smith Co.	Sydney	March 1913
453	T.S.S.	*Bayano* (1st)	6500	417'0" × 53'3" × 32'6"	5948	Elders & Fyffes	London	June 1913
454	T.S.S.	*Gelria*	11300	540'0" × 65'9" × 39'0"	14053	Koninklijke Hollandsche Lloyd	Amsterdam	Oct 1913
455	T.S.S.	*Tubantia*	11300	540'0" × 65'9" × 39'0"	14061	Koninklijke Hollandsche Lloyd	Amsterdam	March 1914
456	S.S.	*Clan Macquarrie*	4050	430'0" × 53'6" × 37'0"	5060	Cayzer Irvine & Co.	Glasgow	Nov. 1913
457	T.S.S.	*Takada*	5200	430'0" × 58'3" × 40'0"	6949	British India S.N. Co.	London	Mar. 1914

Ships built by Alexander Stephen & Sons Ltd, at Linthouse – continued

Yard No.	*Type of Ship*	*Name of Ship*	*H.P.*	*Dimensions*	*Gross Tonnage*	*Built for*	*Owners' Port*	*Completed*
458	T.S.S.	*Tanda*	5200	430'0" × 58'3" × 40'0"	6956	British India S.N. Co.	London	May 1914
459	Twin Geared Turbine	*Tuscania* (1st)	12000	548'0" × 66'6" × 45'0"	14348	Anchor Line	Glasgow	Feb. 1915
460	S.S.	*Umaria*	2700	410'6" × 52'3" × 30'6"	5317	British India S.N. Co.	London	Aug. 1914
461	S.S.	*Umeta*	2700	410'6" × 52'3" × 30'6"	5312	British India S.N. Co.	London	Oct. 1914
462	S.S.	*Chakla*	3150	330'0" × 46'3" × 32'0"	3081	British India S.N. Co.	London	Dec. 1914
463	T.S.S.	*Camito*	6150	425'0" × 54'3" × 32'9"	6611	Elders & Fyffes	London	June 1915
464	T.S.S.	*Bayano* (II)	6230	425'0" × 54'3" × 32'9"	6788	Elders & Fyffes	London	Dec. 1917
465	T.S.S.	*Vasna*	5400	390'0" × 53'3" × 34'3"	5767	British India S.N. Co.	London	June 1917
466	—	—	—	—	—	—	—	—
467	T.S.S.	*Princesa*	7000	430'0" × 61'3" × 38'4½"	8731	Furness Withy & Co.	London	July 1918
468	T.S.S.	*Nariva*	6500	430'0" × 61'3" × 38'6"	8723	Royal Mail S.P. Co.	London	April 1920
469	T.S.S.	*Natia*	6500	430'0" × 61'3" × 38'6"	8723	Royal Mail S.P. Co.	London	Dec. 1920
470	T.B.D.	*Noble*	27800	265'0" × 26'8" × 16'3"	1000	British Admiralty	—	Feb. 1916
471	T.B.D.	*Nizam*	27800	265'0" × 26'8" × 16'3"	1000	British Admiralty	—	June 1916
472	T.B.D.	*Nomad*	27800	265'0" × 26'8" × 16'3"	1000	British Admiralty	—	April 1916
473	T.B.D.	*Non Pareil*	27800	265'0" × 26'8" × 16'3"	1000	British Admiralty	—	June 1916
474	T.S.S.	*Matakana*	5000	477'0" × 63'0" × 42'10"	8048	Shaw Savill & Albion Co.	London	Sept. 1921
475	T.B.D.	*Prince*	27800	265'0" × 26'8" × 16'3"	1000	British Admiralty	—	Sept. 1916
476	T.B.D.	*Pylades*	27800	265'0" × 26'8" × 16'3"	1000	British Admiralty	—	Nov. 1916
477	T.B.D.	*Sturgeon*	31000	265'0" × 26'8" × 16'3"	1000	British Admiralty	—	Feb. 1917
478	T.B.D.	*Sceptre*	31000	265'0" × 26'8" × 16'3"	1000	British Admiralty	—	May 1917
479	T.B.D.	*Tormentor*	31000	265'0" × 26'8" × 16'3"	1000	British Admiralty	—	Aug. 1917

Ships built by Alexander Stephen & Sons Ltd, at Linthouse – continued

Yard No.	Type of Ship	Name of Ship	H.P.	Dimensions	Gross Tonnage	Built for	Owners' Port	Completed
480	T.B.D.	*Tornado*	31000	265'0" × 26'8" × 16'3"	1000	British Admiralty	—	Oct. 1917
481	T.B.D.	*Vesper*	31000	300'0" × 29'7" × 18'3"	1280	British Admiralty	—	Feb. 1918
482	T.B.D.	*Vidette*	31000	300'0" × 29'7" × 18'3"	1280	British Admiralty	—	April 1918
483	T.B.D.	*Voyager*	31000	300'0" × 29'6" × 18'3"	1280	British Admiralty	—	June 1918
484	S.S.	*War Hunter*	3000	400'0" × 52'0" × 31'0"	5222	Shipping Controller	—	Nov. 1918
485	S.S.	*War Gascon*	3000	400'0" × 52'0" × 31'0"	5228	Shipping Controller	—	May 1919
486	S.S.	*War Hussar*	3000	400'0" × 52'0" × 31'0"	5223	Shipping Controller	—	Aug. 1919
487	T.B.D.	*Sabre*	31000	265'0" × 26'8" × 16'3"	1000	British Admiralty	—	Nov. 1918
488	T.B.D.	*Saladin*	31000	265'0" × 26'8" × 16'3"	1000	British Admiralty	—	April 1919
489	T.B.D.	*Sardonyx*	31000	265'0" × 26'8" × 16'3"	1000	British Admiralty	—	July 1919
490	T.B.D.	*Saturn*	—	—	—	—	—	Not Completed
491	T.B.D.	*Sycamore*	—	—	—	—	—	Not Completed
492	S.S.	*Piako*	5000	450'0" × 58'0" × 40'0"	8283	New Zealand Shipping Co.	London	Dec. 1920
493	S.S.	*Tortuguero*	4500	400'0" × 51'0" × 32'11"	5285	Elders & Fyffes	London	Nov. 1921
494	T.S.S.	*California*	13500	550'0" × 70'0" × 42'9"	16792	Anchor Line	Glasgow	Aug. 1923
495	T.S.S.	*Caledonia*	13500	550'0" × 70'0" × 42'9"	17046	Anchor Line	Glasgow	Sept. 1925
496	T.S.S.	*Mulbera*	4000	465'0" × 59'9" × 36'0"	9200	British India S.N. Co.	London	June 1922
497	M.V.	*Dalgoma*	3160	430'0" × 54'6" × 32'4"	5953	British India S.N. Co.	London	May 1923
498	S.S.	*Famaka*	3150	390'0" × 55'0" × 30'0"	5815	Khedivial Mail Steamship Co.	London and Alexandria	Dec. 1922
499	S.S.	*Fezara*	3150	390'0" × 55'0" × 30'0"	5809	Khedivial Mail Steamship Co.	London and Alexandria	Feb. 1923
500	Racing Yacht	*Coila III*	—	6-metre International Class	—	Fred J. Stephen	Glasgow	May 1922

Ships built by Alexander Stephen & Sons Ltd, at Linthouse – continued

Yard No.	*Type of Ship*	*Name of Ship*	*H.P.*	*Dimensions*	*Gross Tonnage*	*Built for*	*Owners' Port*	*Completed*
501	T.S.S.	*Cavina*	4700	425'0" × 54'6" × 32'9"	6908	Elders & Fyffes	London	May 1924
502	S.S.	*Toward*	1770	270'0" × 37'0" × 18'6"	1571	Clyde Shipping Co.	Glasgow	July 1923
503	S.S.	*Bulan*	850	220'0" × 35'0" × 15'0"	1048	P. & O. S.N. Co.	London	June 1924
504	T.S.S.	*Chitral*	11000	525'0" × 70'0" × 46'0"	14997	P. & O. S.N. Co.	London	June 1925
505	S.S.	*The Cable*	1250	228'0" × 35'3" × 24'3"	1534	Eastern Extension, Australasia & China Telegraph Co.	London	Oct. 1924
506	S.S.	*Induna*	1800	402'0" × 52'0" × 29'10"	5086	Maclay & McIntyre	Glasgow	May 1925
507	T.S.S.	*Ariguani*	6200	425'3" × 54'0" × 30'3"	6745	Elders & Fyffes	London	Feb. 1926
508	S.S.	*Britannia*	5400	460'0" × 59'0" × 29'6"	8463	Anchor Line	Glasgow	March 1926
509	Tug	*Forceful*	1000	115'0" × 27'2" × 13'4"	288	Australasian U.S.N. Co.	London and Sydney	Dec. 1925
510	S.S.	*Tucurinca*	3750	400'0" × 51'0" × 33'0"	5411	Elders & Fyffes	London	March 1926
511	Yacht	*Mingary*	400	116'3" × 20'6" × 10'3"	222	Kenneth Clark	Ardnamurchan	June 1926
512	Yacht	*Vadura*	30	65'0" × 19'4" × 13'3"	40	J. H. Maurice Clark	Glasgow	May 1926
513	S.S.	*Chagres* (2nd)	3750	400'0" × 51'0" × 33'0"	5406	Elders & Fyffes	London	Feb. 1928
514	S.S.	*Telde*	2400	300'0" × 44'0" × 25'0"	2519	Elders & Fyffes	London	June 1927
515	S.S.	*Oratava*	2400	300'0" × 44'0" × 25'0"	2518	Elders & Fyffes	London	July 1927
516	Racing Yacht	*Coila IV*	—	8-metre International Class	—	F. J. Stephen	Glasgow	May 1927
517	Oil Tanker	*Victolite*	3300	510'0" × 68'0" × 38'0"	11410	Imperial Oil	Toronto	March 1928
518	Oil Tanker	*Vancolite*	3300	510'0" × 68'0" × 38'0"	11403	Imperial Oil	Toronto	May 1928
519	T.S.S. Turbo-Electric	*Viceroy of India*	17000	612'0" × 76'0" × 45'6"	19648	P. & O. S.N. Co.	London	March 1929
520	S.S.	*Taif*	900	236'0" × 39'3" × 25'6"	1590	Khedivial Mail S.S. Co.	London	June 1928

Ships built by Alexander Stephen & Sons Ltd, at Linthouse – continued

Yard No.	*Type of Ship*	*Name of Ship*	*H.P.*	*Dimensions*	*Gross Tonnage*	*Built for*	*Owners' Port*	*Completed*
521	S.S.	*Talodi*	900	236'0" × 39'3" × 25'6"	1585	Khedivial Mail S.S. Co.	London	June 1928
522	S.S.	*Jumna*	2400	423'6" × 55'9" × 31'4"	6078	James Nourse	London	April 1929
523	S.S.	*Nicoya* (2nd)	3750	400'0" × 51'0" × 33'0"	5363	Elders & Fyffes	London	March 1929
524	S.S.	*Masunda*	2400	402'0" × 54'9" × 31'0"	5250	Maclay & McIntyre	Glasgow	Aug. 1929
525	T.S.S.	*St Patrick*	5500	280'0" × 41'0" × 17'0"	1922	Great Western Railway Co.	London	March 1930
526	Tug	*Carrock*	1000	121'6" × 27'0" × 14'2"	300	Australasian U.S.N. Co.	London and Sydney	Oct. 1929
527	Yacht	*Rover*	3000	265'0" × 40'0" × 23'1"	1851	Earl of Inchcape	Glenapp Castle	July 1930
528	S.S.	*Corrales*	3750	400'0" × 51'0" × 33'0"	5362	Elders & Fyffes	London	March 1930
529	T.S.S.	*Kenya*	10000	470'0" × 64'0" × 41'0"	9890	British India S.N. Co.	London	Dec. 1930
530	T.S.S.	*Karanja*	10000	470'0" × 64'0" × 41'0"	9891	British India S.N. Co.	London	March 1931
531	Motor Ship	*Orari*	9000	470'0" × 67 0" × 40'0"	10106	New Zealand Shipping Co.	London	Feb. 1931
532	Motor Ship	*Opawa*	9000	470'0" × 67 0" × 40'0"	10107	New Zealand Shipping Co.	London	April 1931
533	Yacht	*Golden Hind*	60/80	72'0" × 20'0" × 16'2"	82	Commander Kitson	Loch Hourn	April 1931
534	T.S.S.	*Corfu*	14000	518'6" × 71'0" × 46'0"	14293	P. & O. S.N. Co.	London	Sept. 1931
535	T.S.S.	*Carthage*	14000	518'6" × 71'0" × 46'0"	14305	P. & O. S.N. Co.	London	Nov. 1931
536	Racing Yacht	*Maida*	—	6-metre International Class	—	J. G. Stephen and others	Glasgow	April 1932
537	S.S.	*Gazcon*	2200	394'0" × 52'10" × 34'0½"	4130	Cie De Nav. d'Orbigny	Paris	April 1932
538	Cargo	*Waitaki*	1350	270'0" × 42'6" × 23'0"	2212	Union S.S. Co. of N.Z.	Dunedin	April 1934
539	Aux. Ketch	*Fiumara*	36	55'6" × 17'0" × 11'0"	48	Wm Wordie	Glasgow	May 1934
540	Passenger M.V.	*Manoora*	8400	460'0" × 66'0" × 35'6"	10856	Adelaide S.S. Co.	Melbourne	Feb. 1935
541	Cargo	*Loch Ranza*	2200	412'0" × 56'0" × 37'10"	6889	Maclay & McIntyre	Glasgow	Oct. 1934
542	Aux. Ketch	*Albyn*	46	56'6" × 17'3" × 11'0"	49	Robt French	Glasgow	June 1934

Ships built by Alexander Stephen & Sons Ltd, at Linthouse – continued

Yard No.	*Type of Ship*	*Name of Ship*	*H.P.*	*Dimensions*	*Gross Tonnage*	*Built for*	*Owners' Port*	*Completed*
543	Passenger	*Taroona*	6000	335'0" × 50'0" × 26'3"	4587	Tasmanian Steamers	Melbourne	Jan. 1935
544	T.B.D.	*Gallant*	34000	312'0" × 33'0" × 19'3"	1580	Admiralty	—	Jan. 1936
545	T.B.D.	*Grenade*	34000	312'0" × 33'0" × 19'3"	1580	Admiralty	—	March 1936
546	M.V.	*Karu*	810	220'0" × 35'0" × 16'6"	1044	Union S.S. Co. of N.Z.	Wellington	July 1935
547	Sloop	*Mallard*	3600	234'0" × 26'6" × 14'0"	608	Admiralty	—	June 1936
548	Sloop	*Puffin*	3600	234'0" × 26'6" × 14'0"	608	Admiralty	—	July 1936
549	M.V.	*Kauri*	1600	284'0" × 44'0" × 21'6"	2361	Union S.S. Co. of N.Z.	Wellington	Aug. 1936
550	Coaster	*Rathlin*	1650	270'0" × 38'3" × 18'6"	1600	Clyde Shipping Co.	Glasgow	Oct. 1936
551	Coaster	*Beachy*	1650	270'0" × 38'3" × 18'6"	1600	Clyde Shipping Co.	Glasgow	Nov. 1936
552	T.B.D.	*Zulu*	44000	355'6" × 36'6" × 21'6"	2323	Admiralty	—	March 1938
553	T.B.D.	*Sikh*	44000	355'6" × 36'6" × 21'6"	2323	Admiralty	—	July 1938
554	M.V.	*Waiana*	2400	319'0" × 48'0" × 26'6"	3363	Union S.S. Co. of N.Z.	Dunedin	March 1937
555	Aux. Ketch	*Thendara*	72	72'0" × 20'0" × 13'1"	87	A. S. L. Young	Glasgow	April 1937
556	M.V.	*Kaikoura*	4250	432'0" × 58'9" × 39'5"	5852	N.Z. Shipping Co.	Plymouth	Nov. 1937
557	Passenger	*Canton*	18500	530'0" × 73'0" × 46'0"	16033	P. & O. S.N. Co.	London	Sept. 1938
558	Cargo	*Kakapo*	1570	280'0" × 45'0" × 21'6"	2498	Union S.S. Co. of N.Z.	Wellington	Oct. 1937
559	M.V.	*Wanaka*	2000	275'0" × 45'0" × 21'6"	2259	Union S.S. Co. of N.Z.	Sydney	Feb. 1938
560	Cruiser	*Hermione*	62000	485'0" × 50'0" × 28'3"	—	Admiralty	—	March 1941
561	M.V.	*Surat*	3050	435'0" × 57'6" × 37'3"	5529	Hain S.S. Co.	London	Nov. 1938
562	M.V.	*Shillong*	3050	435'0" × 57'6" × 37'3"	5529	Hain S.S. Co.	London	Feb. 1939
563	Cargo	*Korowai*	1500	290'0" × 45'0" × 21'9"	2525	Union S.S. Co. of N.Z.	Wellington	June 1938
564	Cargo	*Komata*	2640	335'0" × 52'6" × 28'0"	3900	Union S.S. Co. of N.Z.	Wellington	Nov. 1938
565	Cargo	*Kurow*	2640	335'0" × 52'6" × 28'0"	3900	Union S.S. Co. of N.Z.	Wellington	Jan. 1939

Ships built by Alexander Stephen & Sons Ltd, at Linthouse – continued

Yard No.	Type of Ship	Name of Ship	H.P.	Dimensions	Gross Tonnage	Built for	Owners' Port	Completed
566	Cruiser	*Kenya*	80000	538'0" × 61'6" × 32'0"	—	Admiralty	—	Sept. 1940
567	M.V.	*Kaipaki*	4250	432'0" × 58'9" × 39'5"	5862	N.Z. Shipping Co.	Plymouth	April 1939
568	Minelayer	*Manxman*	72000	400'6" × 39'0" × 29'0"	3662	Admiralty	—	June 1941
569	Cruiser	*Ceylon*	80000	538'0" × 61'6" × 32'0"	—	Admiralty	—	July 1943
570	M.V.	*Trevethoe*	1660	425'0" × 56'0" × 36'9"	5257	Hain S.S. Co.	London	June 1940
571	Escort	*Tynedale*	19000	264'3" × 29'0" × 17'2"	—	Admiralty	—	Nov. 1940
572	Escort	*Whaddon*	19000	264'3" × 29'0" × 17'2"	—	Admiralty	—	Feb. 1941
573	T.B.D.	*Matchless*	48000	345'6" × 36'9" × 20'6"	—	Admiralty	—	Feb. 1942
574	T.B.D.	*Meteor*	48000	345'6" × 36'9" × 20'6"	—	Admiralty	—	Aug. 1942
575	Refrig. M.V.	*Gloucester*	6400	450'0" × 60'0" × 39'5"	8532	N.Z. Shipping Co.	London	July 1941
576	Refrig. M.V.	*Nottingham*	6400	450'0" × 60'0" × 39'5"	8532	N.Z. Shipping Co.	London	Nov. 1941
577	Escort	*Croome*	19000	264'3" × 31'6" × 17'2"	—	Admiralty	—	June 1941
578	Escort	*Dulverton*	19000	264'3" × 31'6" × 17'2"	—	Admiralty	—	Sept. 1941
579	Escort	*Blackmore*	19000	264'3" × 31'6" × 17'2"	—	Admiralty	—	April 1942
580	Escort	*Bramham*	19000	264'3" × 31'6" × 17'2"	—	Admiralty	—	June 1942
581	Minesweeper	*Poole*	2000	165'6" × 28'6" × 15'6"	—	Admiralty	—	Oct. 1941
582	Minesweeper	*Lyme Regis*	2000	165'6" × 28'6" × 15'6"	—	Admiralty	—	June 1942
583	M.L.C.	—	80	40'0" × 13'6" × 4'0"	—	Admiralty	—	Dec. 1940
584	M.L.C.	—	80	40'0" × 13'6" × 4'0"	—	Admiralty	—	Dec. 1940
585	M.L.C.	—	80	40'0" × 13'6" × 4'0"	—	Admiralty	—	Dec. 1940
586	M.L.C.	—	80	40'0" × 13'6" × 4'0"	—	Admiralty	—	Dec. 1940
587	T.L.C.	—	500	135'0" × 28'0" × 8'9½"	—	Admiralty	—	Dec. 1940
588	T.L.C.	—	500	135'0" × 28'0" × 8'9½"	—	Admiralty	—	Dec. 1940

Ships built by Alexander Stephen & Sons Ltd, at Linthouse – continued

Yard No.	*Type of Ship*	*Name of Ship*	*H.P.*	*Dimensions*	*Gross Tonnage*	*Built for*	*Owners' Port*	*Completed*
589	Escort	*Holcombe*	19000	264'3" × 31'6" × 17'2"	—	Admiralty	—	Sept. 1942
590	Escort	*Limbourne*	19000	264'3" × 31'6" × 17'2"	—	Admiralty	—	Oct. 1942
591	Minelayer	*Ariadne*	72000	400'6" × 39'0" × 29'0"	—	Admiralty	—	Oct. 1943
592	Refrig. Cargo	*Papanui*	8000	496'6" × 64'6" × 42'0"	10002	N.Z. Shipping Co.	Plymouth	June 1943
593	Refrig. Cargo	*Paparoa*	8000	496'6" × 64'6" × 42'0"	10005	N.Z. Shipping Co.	Plymouth	Dec. 1943
594	Sloop	*Amethyst*	4300	283'0" × 38'6" × 17'6"	—	Admiralty	—	Oct. 1943
595	Sloop	*Hart*	4300	283'0" × 38'6" × 17'6"	—	Admiralty	—	Nov. 1943
596	Cruiser	—	—	Cancelled				
597	Refrig. Cargo	*Pipiriki*	8000	496'6" × 64'6" × 42'0"	10057	N.Z. Shipping Co.	Plymouth	May 1944
598	Aircraft Carrier	*Ocean*	40000	690'0" × 80'0" × 41'6"	—	Admiralty	—	Aug. 1945
599	T.B.D.	*Chevron*	40000	339'6" × 35'8" × 20'6"	—	Admiralty	—	May 1945
600	T.B.D.	*Cheviot*	40000	339'6" × 35'8" × 20'6"	—	Admiralty	—	Dec. 1945
601	T.B.D.	*Consort*	40000	339'6" × 35'8" × 20'6"	—	Admiralty	—	March 1946
602	Refrig. Cargo	*Devon*	8000	469'6" × 64'6" × 42'0"	9940	Federal S.N. Co.	London	Feb. 1946
603	T.B.D.	*Dunkirk*	50000	355'0" × 40'3½" × 22'0"	—	Admiralty	—	Nov. 1946
604	T.B.D.	*Jutland*	50000	355'0" × 40'3½" × 22'0"	—	Admiralty	—	April 1947
605	T.B.D.	*St Lucia*	—	Cancelled				
606	Transport Ferry	*T.F. 3028*	5000	330'0" × 54'0" × 27'0"	—	Admiralty	—	April 1945
607	Transport Ferry	*T.F 3029*	5000	330'0" × 54'0" × 27'0"	—	Admiralty	—	Aug. 1945
608	Refrig. Cargo	*Somerset*	8000	469'6" × 64'6" × 42'0"	9943	Federal S.N. Co.	London	Sept. 1946
609	T.B.D.	*Defender*	54000	366'0" × 43'0" × 22'6"	—	Admiralty	—	—
610	Passenger & Refrig.	*Matina*	7750	420'0" × 57'6" × 35'3"	6801	Elders & Fyffes	Glasgow	Nov. 1946
611	Passenger & Cargo	*Kampala*	8800	480'0" × 66'0" × 41'0"	10304	B.I.S.N. Co.	London	Aug. 1947

Ships built by Alexander Stephen & Sons Ltd, at Linthouse – continued

Yard No.	*Type of Ship*	*Name of Ship*	*H.P.*	*Dimensions*	*Gross Tonnage*	*Built for*	*Owners' Port*	*Completed*
612	Refrig. Cargo M.V.	*Huntingdon*	12800	530'0" × 70'0" × 47'6"	11281	Federal S.N. Co.	London	June 1948
613	Cargo M.V.	*Komata*	2410	325'0" × 50'0" × 26'0"	3543	Union S.S. Co. of N.Z.	Wellington	April 1947
614	Refrig.Cargo M.V.	*Cumberland*	12800	530'0" × 70'0" × 47'6"	11281	Federal S.N. Co.	London	Dec. 1948
615	Cargo M.V.	*Koromiko*	2410	325'0" × 50'0" × 26'0"	3552	Union S.S. Co. of N.Z.	Wellington	Dec. 1947
616	Passenger & Cargo	*Karanja*	8800	480'0" × 66'0" × 41'0"	10294	B.I.S.N. Co.	London	Sept. 1948
617	Cargo M.V.	*Kaitoke*	2410	325'0" × 50'0" × 26'0"	3551	Union S.S. Co. of N.Z.	Dunedin	Sept. 1948
618	Passenger & Refrig.	*Golfito*	10800	415'0" × 62'0" × 34'9"	8736	Elders & Fyffes	Glasgow	Nov. 1949
619	Passenger & Refrig. M.V.	*Fort Richepanse*	8000	375'0" × 52'3" × 29'3½"	5050	Compagnie Générale Transatlantique, France	Le Havre	July 1949
620	Passenger & Refrig. M.V.	*Fort Dauphin*	8000	375'0" × 52'3" × 29'3½"	5050	Compagnie Générale Transatlantique, France	Le Havre	Nov. 1949
621	Refrig.Cargo	*Dorset*	8000	469'6" × 64'6" × 42'0"	10108	Federal S.N. Co.	London	Nov. 1949
622	Refrig.Cargo M.V.	*Rio Bermejo*	5900	460'0" × 62'0" × 38'0"	7143	Argentine Government	Buenos Aires	April 1950
623	Cargo	*Dunedin Star*	8000	469'6" × 64'6" × 42'0"	7322	Blue Star Line	London	Sept. 1950
624	CargoM.V.	*Kawaroa*	2410	325'0" × 50'0" × 26'0"	3532	Union S.S. Co. of N.Z.	Wellington	June 1950
625	Cargo	*City of Bedford*	5500	450'0" × 61'6" × 41'3"	7050	Ellerman Lines	Liverpool	Nov. 1950
626	Cargo	*City of Singapore*	5500	450'0" × 61'6" × 41'3"	7050	Ellerman Lines	Liverpool	Feb. 1951
627	Refrig. Cargo M.V.	*Cornwall*	7600	460'0" × 62'0" × 40'3"	7560	Federal S.N. Co	London	Feb. 1952
628	Passenger and Cargo M.V.	*Aureol*	8000	480'0" × 70'0" × 36'6"	13110	Elder Dempster Lines	Liverpool	Oct. 1951
629	Unallocated?							
630	Refrig. Cargo M.V.	*Surrey*	8500	469'6" × 64'6" × 42'0"	8320	Federal S.N.Co.	London	June 1952
631	Refrig. Cargo M.V.	*Middlesex*	8500	469'6" × 64'6" × 42'0"	8320	Federal S.N.Co.	London	April 1953

Ships built by Alexander Stephen & Sons Ltd, at Linthouse – continued

Yard No.	*Type of Ship*	*Name of Ship*	*H.P.*	*Dimensions*	*Gross Tonnage*	*Built for*	*Owners' Port*	*Completed*
632	Cargo M.V.	*Kurutai*	2410	325'0" × 50'0" × 26'0"	3530	Union S.S. Co. of N.Z.	Wellington	July 1952
633	Cargo M.V.	*Enton*	5000	432'0" × 58'9" × 39'6"	6350	Birt, Potter & Hughes	London	May 1952
634	Cargo M.V.	*Kowhai*	2410	325'0" × 50'0" × 26'0"	3530	Union S.S. Co. of N.Z.	Wellington	Sep. 1952
635	General Cargo M.V.	*Waimea*	2410	325'0" × 50'0" × 26'0"	3657	Union S.S. Co. of N.Z.	Dunedin	March 1953
636	Passenger and Cargo	*Olympia*	24000	560'0" × 79'0" × 47'0"	22979	Goulandris Bros	Monrovia	Oct. 1953
637	Refrigerated Cargo	*Patonga*	9000	469'6" × 64'6" × 42'0"	10070	P. & O. S.N. Co.	London	Nov. 1953
638	Frigate	*Murray*	15000	300'0" × 33'0" × 18'6"	1495	Admiralty	—	June 1956
639	Frigate	*Palliser*	15000	300'0" × 33'0" × 18'6"	1497	Admiralty	—	Dec. 1957
640	Passenger and Refrig. Cargo M.V.	*Whakatane*	7100	439'4" × 62'9" × 39'6"	8726	N.Z. Shipping Co.	London	May 1954
641	Cargo	*Ballarat*	13000	490'0" × 69'0" × 43'0"	8792	P. & O. S.N. Co.	London	July 1954
642	Cargo	*Bendigo*	13000	490'0" × 69'0" × 43'0"	8782	P. & O. S.N. Co.	London	Nov. 1954
643	Pass. and Cargo M.V.	*Irma*	4400	400'0" × 57'0" × 35'0"	4442	Bergenske D/S	Bergen	Dec. 1954
644	Pass. and Cargo M.V.	*Fernvalley*	4400	400'0" × 57'0" × 35'0"	4504	Fearnley & Eger	Oslo	March 1955
645	Cargo	*Castilian*	3150	350'6" × 53'0" × 32'9"	3803	Ellerman Lines	Liverpool	July 1955
646	Train and Passenger M.V.	*Princess of Vancouver*	5600	388'0" × 63'0" × 37'6"	5554	Canadian Pacific S.S. Co.	Victoria B.C.	April 1955
647	Cargo M.V.	*Kawerau*	2410	325'0" × 50'0" × 26'0"	3598	Union S.S. Co. of N.Z.	Auckland	Sep. 1955
648	Cargo M.V.	*Kaimiro*	2410	325'0" × 50'0" × 26'0"	3722	Union S.S. Co. of N.Z.	Dunedin	March 1956
649	Passenger & Refrig.	*Camito*	10500	415'0" × 62'0" × 34'9"	8687	Elders & Fyffes	Glasgow	Nov. 1956
650	Cargo M.V.	*City of Newcastle*	8000	470'0" × 65'6" × 42'0"	7727	Ellerman Lines	Liverpool	March 1956
651	Refrig. Cargo M.V.	*City of Melbourne*	14000	510'0" × 71'0" × 43'6"	9914	Ellerman Lines	London	Aug. 1959
652	Refrig. Cargo M.V.	*Crux*	4400	400'0" × 57'0" × 35'0"	4429	Bergenske D/S	Bergen	Sep. 1956

Ships built by Alexander Stephen & Sons Ltd, at Linthouse – continued

Yard No.	*Type of Ship*	*Name of Ship*	*H.P.*	*Dimensions*	*Gross Tonnage*	*Built for*	*Owners' Port*	*Completed*
653	Cargo M.V.	*Kaituna*	2410	325'0" × 50'0" × 26'0"	3722	Union S.S. Co. of N.Z.	Auckland	July 1956
654	Cargo M.V.	*Koranui*	2410	325'0" × 50'0" × 26'0"	3722	Union S.S. Co. of N.Z.	Auckland	Nov. 1956
655	Frigate	*Kirpan*	15000	300'0" × 33'0" × 18'6"	—	Indian Navy	—	July 1959
656	Cargo M.V.	*Donegal*	5500	432'0" × 58'9" × 39'6"	6327	Avenue Shipping Co.	London	March 1957
657	Refrig. and Passenger	*Changuinola*	8300	390'0" × 56'6" × 35'0"	6283	Elders & Fyffes	Glasgow	Sep. 1957
658	Refrig. and Passenger	*Chirripo*	8300	390'0" × 56'6" × 35'0"	6283	Elders & Fyffes	Glasgow	Dec 1957
659	Refrig. and Passenger	*Chicanoa*	8300	390'0" × 56'6" × 35'0"	6283	Elders & Fyffes	Glasgow	March 1958
660	Cargo M.V.	*Koraki*	2410	325'0" × 51'0" × 26'0"	3790	Union S.S. Co. of N.Z.	Wellington	Sep. 1957
661	Cargo M.V.	*Katea*	2410	325'0" × 51'0" × 26'0"	3790	Union S.S. Co. of N.Z.	Wellington	June 1958
662	Refrig. Cargo M.V.	*Chatham*	4250	310'0" × 47'0" × 26'6"	3005	Blue Star Line	Liverpool	Feb. 1960
663	Cargo M.V.	*Risdon*	2410	335'0" × 51'6" × 26'6"	4125	Union S.S. Co. of N.Z.	Hobart	May 1959
664	Oil Tanker M.V.	*British Fulmar*	7750	495'0" × 69'0" × 27'0"	11169	B.P. Tanker Co.	London	Feb. 1959
665	Cargo M.V.	*Waikare*	2410	325'0" × 50'0" × 26'0"	3839	Union S.S. Co. of N.Z.	Auckland	Sep. 1958
666	Frigate	*Lowestoft*	—	360'0" × 41'0" × 28'3"	2515	Admiralty	—	Oct. 1961
667	Oil Tanker	*Mobil Acme*	9250	525'0" × 74'0" × 39'0"	12751	Mobil Tanker Co.	London	May 1960
668	Oil Tanker	*Mobil Apex*	9250	525'0" × 74'0" × 39'0"	12751	Mobil Tanker Co.	London	Dec. 1960
669	Frigate	*President Steyn*	—	360'0" × 41'0" × 26'0"	2515	South African Navy	—	March 1963
670	Oil Tanker M.V.	*British Curlew*	7750	495'0" × 69'0" × 27'0"	11157	B.P. Tanker Co.	London	June 1960
671	Refrig. Cargo M.V.	*Iberic*	11300	481'0" × 70'0" × 41'6"	11248	Shaw Savill	S'hampton	April 1961
672	Oil Tanker	*British Bombardier*	16000	725'0" × 97'0" × 54'0"	32351	B.P. Tanker Co.	London	Sep. 1962
673	Cargo M.V.	*Antrim*	5500	432'0" × 58'9" × 39'6"	6330	Avenue Shipping Co.	London	April 1962
674	Frigate	*Zulu*	20002	350'0" × 41'6" × 27'6"	—	Admiralty	—	April 1964
675	Refrig. & Passenger	*Chuscal*	9000	390'0" × 56'6" × 35'0"	6283	Elders & Fyffes	Glasgow	March 1961

Ships built by Alexander Stephen & Sons Ltd, at Linthouse – continued

Yard No.	*Type of Ship*	*Name of Ship*	*H.P.*	*Dimensions*	*Gross Tonnage*	*Built for*	*Owners' Port*	*Completed*
676	Refrig. Cargo M.V.	*Piako*	10400	460'0" × 66'0" × 41'0"	9985	N.Z. Shipping Co.	London	Jan. 1962
677	Cargo	*Dumurra*	4700	430'0" × 63'0" × 38'6"	6180	Elder Dempster	Liverpool	July 1961
678	Cargo M.V.	*Markhor*	10000	450'0" × 68'0" × 38'6"	6867	Brocklebank	Liverpool	Jan. 1963
679	Cargo M.V.	*Mahout*	10000	450'0" × 68'0" × 38'6"	6894	Brocklebank	Liverpool	June 1963
680	Cross Channel Ferry	*Avalon*	13500	372'0" × 57'6" × 21'0"	6719	British Transport Co.	Harwich	Aug. 1963
681	Frigate	*Phoebe*	30000	360'0" × 42'0" × 28'3"		M.O.D. (Navy)	—	April 1968
682	Suction Hopper Dredger	*Skitterness*	1500	216'0" × 44'0" × 19'0"	1577	British Transport Docks Board	Hull	Dec. 1963
683	Offshore Sternwell Tin Dredger	*Banka 1*	Non-prop	300'0" × 80'0" × 19'6"	3130	Central Management Board, Indonesia	—	Nov. 1965
684	Refrig. Cargo M.V.	*Zealandic*	11130	440'0" × 65'6" × 37'9"	7946	Shaw Savill	London	March 1964
685	Cargo M.V.	*Melbrook*[1]	7700	430'0" × 66'0" × 42'0"	11075	Duff, Herbert & Mitchell	Newcastle -on-Tyne	Aug. 1964
686	Suction Hopper Dredger	*Severodvinski*	1800	252'0" × 45'0" × 17'0"	1972	Sudoimport U.S.S.R.	Archangel	Sep. 1966
687	Suction Hopper Dredger	*Onegski*	1800	252'0" × 45'0" × 17'0"	1972	Sudoimport U.S.S.R.	Archangel	Nov. 1966
688	Suction Hopper Dredger	*Arabatski*	1800	252'0" × 45'0" × 17'0"	1972	Sudoimport U.S.S.R.	Odessa	Dec. 1966
689	Cutter Suction Dredger	*Nassau Bay*	Non-prop	195'0" × 46'0" × 13'3"	1125	Construction Plant Facilities	London	May 1965
690	Logistic Support	*Sir Galahad*	9400	366'3" × 58'0" × 26'0"	6617	Sea Transport	London	Dec. 1966

1. Started by Denny's of Dumbarton as spec. ship. Completed by Stephen's after Denny's went into liquidation.

Ships built by Alexander Stephen & Sons Ltd, at Linthouse – continued

Yard No.	Type of Ship	Name of Ship	H.P.	Dimensions	Gross Tonnage	Built for	Owners' Port	Completed
691	Logistic Support	*Sir Geraint*	9400	366'3" × 58'0" × 26'0"	6617	Sea Transport	London	July 1967
692	Diesel Electric[1] Bucket Dredger	*Nikarshaka*	Non-prop	140'0" × 33'0" × 11'0"	667	Bombay Port Trust	Bombay	—
693	T.S. Hopper Barge[1]	—	1400	175'0" × 35'0" × 16'3"	976	Calcutta Port Commissioners	Calcutta	—
694	T.S. Hopper Barge[1]	—	1400	175'0" × 35'0" × 16'3"	976	Calcutta Port Commissioners	Calcutta	—
695	Refrig. Cargo M.V.	*Majestic*	15000	500'0" × 74'0" × 45'6"	12591	Shaw Savill	Southampton	Jan. 1967
696	Refrig. Cargo M.V.	*Britannic*	15000	500'0" × 74'0" × 45'6"	12228	Shaw Savill	Southampton	Nov. 1967
697	Frigate	*Hermione*	30000	260'0" × 43'0" × 28'3"	—	M.O.D. (Navy)	—	July 1969
698	Suction Hopper Dredger	*Ribbok*	3600	349'0" × 59'0" × 28'0"	4390	South African Railways	Durban	July 1967
699	Not allocated							
700	Refrig. Cargo M.V.	*Port Chalmers*	26000	570'0" × 81'0" × 48'6"	16283	Port Line	London	April 1968
701	Refrig. Cargo M.V.	*Port Caroline*	26000	570'0" × 81'0" × 48'6"	16283	Port Line	London	Oct. 1968
—	Bucket Tin Dredger[2]	—	Non-prop	95'0" × 45'0" × 9'0"		de Lozada Bros.	Bolivia	—
—	Bucket Dredger[3]	—	Non-prop	140'0" × 33'0" × 11'0"	667	Bombay Port Trust	Bombay	—

1. Built in India to Simons Lobnitz design with special machinery also supplied.
2. Built 'piece small', transported and erected in Bolivia similarly to Ship No.138 *Aurora del Titicaca*.
3. Built 'piece small'.

Index

Names of ships shown in italics